Non-League Football Supporters' Guide & Yearbook 2012

EDITOR
John Robinson

Twentieth Edition

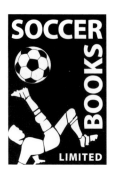

For details of our range of over 1,900 books and 400 DVDs, visit our web site or contact us using the information shown below.

British Library Cataloguing in Publication Data
A catalogue record for this book is available from the British Library

ISBN: 978-1-86223-220-4

Manufactured in the UK by Charlesworth Press, Wakefield

FOREWORD

Our thanks go to the numerous club officials who have aided us in the compilation of information contained in this guide and also to Michael Robinson (page layouts), Bob Budd (cover artwork), Tony Brown (Cup Statistics – www.soccerdata.com) and Derek Mead for providing some of the photographs.

Any readers who have up-to-date ground photographs which they would like us to consider for use in a future edition of this guide are requested to contact us at our address which is shown on the facing page.

Shortly before publication of this book, we received the news that Kettering Town FC would in future play their fixtures at Nene Park, the former home of Rushden & Diamonds FC, a club which suffered severe financial problems and was expelled from the Football Conference as a consequence in June 2011. Because of this late alteration, Kettering Town FC asked us to point out that their admission prices may be subject to change during the 2011/2012 season and details of their club shop will be finalised as soon as is practicable.

The fixtures listed later in this book were released just a short time before we went to print and, as such, some of the dates shown may be subject to change. We therefore suggest that readers treat these fixtures as a rough guide and check dates carefully before attending matches.

Finally, we would like to wish our readers a safe and happy spectating season.

John Robinson
EDITOR

CONTENTS

THE FOOTBALL CONFERENCE BLUE SQUARE PREMIER

Address   Third Floor, Wellington House, 31-34 Waterloo Street, Birmingham   B2 5TJ

Phone (0121) 214-1950

Web site   www.footballconference.co.uk

Clubs for the 2011/2012 Season

AFC TELFORD UNITED

Founded: 2004
Former Names: Formed after Telford United FC went out of business. TUFC were previously known as Wellington Town FC
Nickname: 'The Bucks'
Ground: The New Bucks Head Stadium, Watling Street, Wellington, Telford TF1 2TU
Record Attendance: 13,000 (1935)

Pitch Size: 110 × 74 yards
Colours: White shirts with Black shorts
Telehone Nº: (01952) 640064
Fax Number: (01952) 640021
Ground Capacity: 5,780
Seating Capacity: 2,280
Web site: www.telfordutd.co.uk

GENERAL INFORMATION
Car Parking: At the ground
Coach Parking: At the ground
Nearest Railway Station: Wellington
Nearest Bus Station: Wellington
Club Shop: At the ground
Opening Times: Tuesdays and Thursdays 4.00pm to 6.00pm and Saturday Matchdays from 1.30pm
Telephone Nº: None

GROUND INFORMATION
Away Supporters' Entrances & Sections:
Frank Nagington Stand on the rare occasions when segregation is used

ADMISSION INFO (2011/2012 PRICES)
Adult Standing: £13.00
Adult Seating: £13.00
Under-14s Standing: £1.00 (with a paying adult)
Under-14s Seating: £1.00 (with a paying adult)
Under-18s Standing/Seating: £5.00
Senior Citizen Standing: £10.00
Senior Citizen Seating: £10.00
Programme Price: £2.00

DISABLED INFORMATION
Wheelchairs: Accommodated at both ends of the ground
Helpers: Admitted
Prices: Normal prices apply
Disabled Toilets: Available
Contact: (01952) 640064 (Bookings are not necessary)

Travelling Supporters' Information:
Routes: Exit the M54 at Junction 6 and take the A518. Go straight on at the first roundabout, take the second exit at the next roundabout then turn left at the following roundabout. Follow the road round to the right then turn left into the car park.

ALFRETON TOWN FC |

Founded: 1959
Former Names: None
Nickname: 'Reds'
Ground: The Impact Arena, North Street, Alfreton, Derbyshire DE55 7FZ
Record Attendance: 5,023 vs Matlock Town (1960)
Pitch Size: 110 × 75 yards

Colours: Red shirts and shorts
Telephone Nº: (0115) 939-2090
Fax Number: (0115) 949-1846
Ground Capacity: 4,238
Seating Capacity: 1,600
Web site: www.alfretontownfc.com

GENERAL INFORMATION
Car Parking: At the ground
Coach Parking: Available close to the ground
Nearest Railway Station: Alfreton (½ mile)
Nearest Bus Station: Alfreton (5 minutes walk)
Club Shop: At the ground
Opening Times: Matchdays only
Telephone Nº: (01773) 830277

GROUND INFORMATION
Away Supporters' Entrances & Sections:
Segregation is usual so please check with stewards when arriving at the game.

ADMISSION INFO (2011/2012 PRICES)
Adult Standing: £10.00
Adult Seating: £10.00
Senior Citizen/Junior Standing: £5.00
Senior Citizen/Junior Seating: £5.00
Programme Price: £2.00

DISABLED INFORMATION
Wheelchairs: Accommodated in dedicated areas of the ground
Helpers: Admitted
Prices: Please phone the club for information
Disabled Toilets: Available
Contact: (01773) 830277 (Bookings are not necessary)

Travelling Supporters' Information:
Routes: Exit the M1 at Junction 28 and take the A38 signposted for Derby. After 2 miles take the sliproad onto the B600 then go right at the main road towards the town centre. After ½ mile turn left down North Street and the ground is on the right after 200 yards.

BARROW FC

Founded: 1901
Former Names: None
Nickname: 'Bluebirds'
Ground: Holker Street Stadium, Barrow-in-Furness, Cumbria   LA14 5UW
Record Attendance: 16,874 (1954)
Pitch Size: 110 × 75 yards

Colours: White shirts with Blue shorts
Telephone Nº: (01229) 823061
Fax Number: (01229) 823061
Ground Capacity: 4,057
Seating Capacity: 928
Web site: www.barrowafc.com

GENERAL INFORMATION

Car Parking: Street Parking, Popular Side Car Park and Soccer Bar Car Park
Coach Parking: Adjacent to the ground
Nearest Railway Station: Barrow Central (½ mile)
Nearest Bus Station: ½ mile
Club Shop: At the ground
Opening Times: Monday to Friday 9.00am – 3.30pm and Saturdays 10.00am – 2.00pm
Telephone Nº: (01229) 823061

GROUND INFORMATION

Away Supporters' Entrances & Sections:
West Terrace (not covered)

ADMISSION INFO (2011/2012 PRICES)

Adult Standing: £14.00
Adult Seating: £15.00
Concessionary Standing: £11.00
Concessionary Seating: £12.00
Under-16s Standing/Seating: £6.00
Under-7s Standing/Seating: £3.00
Programme Price: £2.00

DISABLED INFORMATION

Wheelchairs: 6 spaces available in the Disabled Area
Helpers: Admitted
Prices: Normal prices apply
Disabled Toilets: Available
Contact: (01229) 823061   (Bookings are not necessary)

Travelling Supporters' Information:
Routes: Exit the M6 at Junction 36 and take the A590 through Ulverston. Using the bypass, follow signs for Barrow. After approximately 5 miles, turn left into Wilkie Road and the ground is on the right.

BATH CITY FC

Founded: 1889
Former Names: Bath AFC, Bath Railway FC and Bath Amateurs FC
Nickname: 'The Romans'
Ground: Twerton Park, Bath   BA2 1DB
Record Attendance: 18,020 (1960)
Pitch Size: 110 × 76 yards

Colours: Black and White striped shirts, Black shorts
Telephone Nº: (01225) 423087/313247
Fax Number: (01225) 481391
Ground Capacity: 8,840
Seating Capacity: 1,026
Web site: www.bathcityfc.com

GENERAL INFORMATION

Car Parking: 150 spaces available at the ground
Coach Parking: Available at the ground
Nearest Railway Station: Oldfield Park (1 mile)
Nearest Bus Station: Avon Street, Bath
Club Shop: Yes – contact Martin Brush, c/o Club
Opening Times: Matchdays and office hours
Telephone Nº: (01225) 423087

GROUND INFORMATION

Away Supporters' Entrances & Sections:
Turnstiles 17-19

ADMISSION INFO (2011/2012 PRICES)

Adult Standing: £14.00
Adult Seating: £15.00
Senior Citizen Standing: £9.00
Senior Citizen Seating: £10.00
Under-16s Standing: £4.00
Under-16s Seating: £5.00
Programme Price: £2.50

DISABLED INFORMATION

Wheelchairs: 10 spaces available each for home and away fans in front of the Family Stand
Helpers: Admitted
Prices: £9.00 for the disabled. Free entrance for helpers
Disabled Toilets: Available behind the Family Stand
Contact: (01225) 423087   (Bookings are not necessary)

Travelling Supporters' Information:
Route: As a recommendation, avoid exiting the M4 at Junction 18 as the road from takes you through Bath City Centre. Instead, exit the M4 at Junction 19 onto the M32. Turn off the M32 at Junction 1 and follow the A4174 Bristol Ring Road south then join the A4 for Bath. On the A4, after passing through Saltford you will reach a roundabout shortly before entering Bath. Take the 2nd exit at this roundabout then follow the road before turning left into Newton Road at the bottom of the steep hill. The ground is then on the right hand side of the road.

BRAINTREE TOWN FC

Founded: 1898
Former Names: Manor Works FC, Crittall Athletic FC, Braintree & Crittall Athletic FC and Braintree FC
Nickname: 'The Iron'
Ground: Cressing Road Stadium, Clockhouse Way, Braintree, Essex   CM7 3RD
Record Attendance: 4,000 (May 1952)
Pitch Size: 111 × 78 yards

Ground Capacity: 4,151
Seating Capacity: 556
Colours: Orange shirts and socks with Blue shorts
Telephone Nº: (01376) 345617
Fax Number: (01376) 330976
Correspondence Address: Tom Woodley, 19A Bailey Bridge Road, Braintree   CM7 5TT
Contact Telephone Nº: (01376) 326234
Web site: www.braintreetownfc.org.uk

GENERAL INFORMATION

Car Parking: At the ground
Coach Parking: At the ground
Nearest Railway Station: Braintree (1 mile)
Nearest Bus Station: Braintree
Club Shop: At the ground
Opening Times: Matchdays only
Telephone Nº: (01376) 345617

GROUND INFORMATION

Away Supporters' Entrances & Sections:
Gates 7-8

ADMISSION INFO (2011/2012 PRICES)

Adult Standing: £15.00
Adult Seating: £16.00
Senior Citizen Standing: £10.00
Under-16s Standing: £5.00
Under-11s Standing: £3.00
Programme Price: £2.00

DISABLED INFORMATION

Wheelchairs: Accommodated
Helpers: Admitted
Prices: Normal prices apply
Disabled Toilets: Available
Contact: (01376) 345617

Travelling Supporters' Information:
Routes: Exit the A120 Braintree Bypass at the McDonald's roundabout following signs for East Braintree Industrial Estate. The floodlights at the ground are visible on the left ½ mile into town. Turn left into Clockhouse Way then left again for the ground.

CAMBRIDGE UNITED FC

Founded: 1912	**Pitch Size**: 110 × 74 yards
Former Name: Abbey United FC (1912-1951)	**Record Attendance**: 14,000 (1st May 1970)
Nickname: 'U's' 'United'	**Colours**: Amber shirts, Black shorts
Ground: The R Costings Abbey Stadium,	**Telephone Nº**: (01223) 566500
Newmarket Road, Cambridge CB5 8LN	**Ticket Office**: (01223) 566500
Ground Capacity: 8,339	**Fax Number**: (01223) 729220
Seating Capacity: 4,376	**Web Site**: www.cambridgeunited.com

GENERAL INFORMATION

Car Parking: Street parking only
Coach Parking: Coldhams Road
Nearest Railway Station: Cambridge (2 miles)
Nearest Bus Station: Cambridge City Centre
Club Shop: At the ground
Opening Times: Monday to Friday 9.30am to 4.00pm and Matchdays 11.00am to kick-off
Telephone Nº: (01223) 566500

GROUND INFORMATION

Away Supporters' Entrances & Sections:
Coldham Common turnstiles 20-22 – Habbin Terrace (South) and South Stand (Seating) turnstiles 23-26

ADMISSION INFO (2011/2012 PRICES)

Adult Standing: £14.00
Adult Seating: £16.00 – £17.00
Child Standing: £5.00
Child Seating: £5.00 (in the Family Stand) or £5.00–£8.00
Concessionary Standing: £10.00
Concessionary Seating: £11.00 – £12.00
Programme Price: £3.00

DISABLED INFORMATION

Wheelchairs: 19 spaces in total for Home fans in the disabled sections, in front of Main Stand and in the North Terrace. 16 spaces for Away fans in the South Stand.
Helpers: One helper admitted per disabled fan
Prices: £9.00 for the disabled. Free of charge for helpers
Disabled Toilets: At the rear of the disabled section
Contact: (01223) 566500   (Early booking strongly advised)

Travelling Supporters' Information: From the North: Take the A14 from Huntingdon, then turn east along the A14 dual carriageway. Exit the A14 at the 4th junction (to the east of Cambridge), up the slip road signposted Stow-cum-Quy then turn right onto the A1303, returning westwards towards Cambridge. Go straight on at the first roundabout passing the Airport on the left then straight on at two sets of traffic lights. Go straight on at the next roundabout and the ground is on the left after 700 yards; From the South: Exit the M11 at Junction 14 and turn east along the A14 dual carriageway. Then as from the North.
Bus Services: Services from the Railway Station to the City Centre and Nº 3 from the City Centre to the Ground.

DARLINGTON FC

Founded: 1883
Nickname: 'Quakers'
Ground: Darlington Arena, Hurworth Moor, Neasham Road, Darlington DL2 1DL
Ground Capacity: 25,321 (All seats)
Record Attendance: 10,224 (16th August 2003)
Pitch Size: 115 × 74 yards

Colours: White and Black shirts with White shorts
Telephone Nº: (01325) 387000
Ticket Office: 0871 855-1883
Fax Number: (01325) 387015
Web Site: www.darlington-fc.net

GENERAL INFORMATION

Car Parking: Limited number of spaces at the ground
Coach Parking: At the ground
Nearest Railway Station: Darlington (1½ miles)
Nearest Bus Station: Darlington Central
Club Shop: At the ground
Opening Times: Monday to Friday 10.00am – 5.00pm and Saturday matchdays 10.00am – 3.00pm
Telephone Nº: (01325) 387020

GROUND INFORMATION

Away Supporters' Entrances & Sections:
East Stand

ADMISSION INFO (2011/2012 PRICES)

Adult Seating: £16.00 (Matchday price £18.00)
Senior Citizen/Student Seating: £10.00 (Matchday £12)
Under-16s Seating: £5.00
Note: Price reductions are available if tickets are pre-booked
Programme Price: £2.50

DISABLED INFORMATION

Wheelchairs: Spaces available in disabled sections throughout the ground. Lifts are available in the stands
Helpers: One helper admitted per disabled person
Prices: £10.00 for the disabled and blind (£12.00 if purchased on the Matchday). Free of charge for helpers
Disabled Toilets: Available in all stands
Contact: (01325) 387000

Travelling Supporters' Information:
Routes: From All Parts: Take the A1 to the A66(M) and follow the road to it's end. Take the 1st exit at the roundabout, go up the hill then, at the second roundabout, take the 3rd exit signposted A66 Teeside. The ground is at the next roundabout after approximately 1 mile.

EBBSFLEET UNITED FC

Founded: 1946
Former Names: Gravesend & Northfleet United FC, Gravesend United FC and Northfleet United FC
Nickname: 'The Fleet'
Ground: Stonebridge Road, Northfleet, Gravesend, Kent DA11 9GN
Record Attendance: 12,063 (1963)

Colours: Reds shirts with White shorts
Telephone Nº: (01474) 533796
Fax Number: (01474) 324754
Pitch Size: 112 × 72 yards
Ground Capacity: 5,258
Seating Capacity: 1,220
Web site: www.ebbsfleetunited.co.uk

GENERAL INFORMATION

Car Parking: Ebbsfleet International Car Park C (when available) and also street parking
Coach Parking: At the ground
Nearest Railway Station: Northfleet (5 minutes walk)
Nearest Bus Station: Bus Stop outside the ground
Club Shop: At the ground
Opening Times: Matchdays only
Telephone Nº: (01474) 533796

GROUND INFORMATION

Away Supporters' Entrances & Sections:
Only some games are segregated – contact club for details

ADMISSION INFO (2011/2012 PRICES)

Adult Standing: £15.00
Adult Seating: £17.00
Concessionary Standing: £7.00
Concessionary Seating: £9.00
Programme Price: £2.50

DISABLED INFORMATION

Wheelchairs: 6 spaces are available in the Disabled Area in front of the Main Stand
Helpers: Admitted free of charge
Prices: Please phone the club for information
Disabled Toilets: Available in the Main Stand
Contact: (01474) 533796 (Bookings are necessary)

Travelling Supporters' Information:
Routes: Take the A2 to the Northfleet/Southfleet exit and follow signs for Northfleet (B262). Go straight on at the first roundabout then take the 2nd exit at the 2nd roundabout into Thames Way and follow the football signs for the ground.

FLEETWOOD TOWN FC

Founded: 1977
Former Names: None (The club succeeded Fleetwood FC who existed from 1907-1977)
Nickname: 'The Fishermen'
Ground: Highbury Stadium, Park Avenue, Fleetwood FY7 6TX
Record Attendance: 6,150 vs Rochdale FC (1965)

Pitch Size: 112 × 71 yards
Colours: Red shirts with White sleeves, White shorts
Telephone No: (01253) 770702
Fax Number: (01253) 770702
Ground Capacity: 3,450
Seating Capacity: 550
Web site: www.fleetwoodtownfc.com

GENERAL INFORMATION

Car Parking: Spaces for 40 cars at the ground and also street parking
Coach Parking: At the ground
Nearest Railway Station: Poulton (7 miles)
Nearest Bus Station: Fleetwood
Club Shop: Sales via the club web site only
Opening Times: None
Telephone No: –

GROUND INFORMATION

Away Supporters' Entrances & Sections:
No usual segregation

ADMISSION INFO (2011/2012 PRICES)

Adult Standing: £15.00
Adult Seating: £17.00 – £18.00
Under-16s Standing: £10.00
Under-16s Seating: £12.00 – £13.00
Senior Citizen Standing: £11.00
Senior Citizen Seating: £13.00 – £14.00
Note: Discounts are available for tickets purchased in advance
Programme Price: £2.50

DISABLED INFORMATION

Wheelchairs: Accommodated
Helpers: Admitted
Prices: Normal prices apply for the disabled and helpers
Disabled Toilets: Available
Contact: (01253) 770702 (Bookings are necessary)

Travelling Supporters' Information:
Routes: Exit the M55 at Junction 3 and take the A585 to Fleetwood (approximately 11½ miles). Upon reaching Fleetwood, take the 1st exit at the Nautical College roundabout (with the statue of Eros in the middle) and continue for about 1 mile to the next roundabout. Take the 6th exit onto Hatfield Avenue and after about ½ mile (when the road bends to the right)m turn left into Nelson Road. The ground is situated on the left after 100 yards.

FOREST GREEN ROVERS FC

Founded: 1889
Former Names: Stroud FC
Nickname: 'The Rovers'
Ground: The New Lawn, Smiths Way,
Forest Green, Nailsworth, Gloucestershire, GL6 0FG
Record Attendance: 4,836 (3rd January 2009)
Pitch Size: 110 × 70 yards

Colours: Black and White striped shirts, Black shorts
Telephone Nº: (01453) 834860
Fax Number: (01453) 835291
Ground Capacity: 5,147
Seating Capacity: 2,500
Web site: www.forestgreenroversfc.com

GENERAL INFORMATION

Car Parking: At the ground
Coach Parking: At the ground
Nearest Railway Station: Stroud (4 miles)
Nearest Bus Station: Nailsworth
Club Shop: At the ground
Opening Times: Matchdays only
Telephone Nº: (01453) 834860

GROUND INFORMATION

Away Supporters' Entrances & Sections:
EESI Stand

ADMISSION INFO (2011/2012 PRICES)

Adult Standing: £13.00
Adult Seating: £15.00
Senior Citizen Standing: £8.00
Senior Citizen Seating: £10.00
Child Standing: £3.00
Child Seating: £3.00
Programme Price: £2.50

DISABLED INFORMATION

Wheelchairs: Accommodated in the Main Stand
Helpers: Admitted
Prices: Normal prices for the disabled. Free for helpers
Disabled Toilets: Yes
Contact: (01453) 834860 (Enquiries necessary at least 72 hours in advance)

Travelling Supporters' Information:
Routes: The ground is located 4 miles south of Stroud on the A46 to Bath. Upon entering Nailsworth, turn into Spring Hill at the mini-roundabout and the ground is approximately ½ mile up the hill on the left.

GATESHEAD FC

Founded: 1930   (Reformed in 1977)
Former Names: Gateshead United FC
Nickname: 'Tynesiders'
Ground: International Stadium, Neilson Road, Gateshead   NE10 0EF
Record Attendance: 11,750 (1995)
Pitch Size: 110 × 70 yards

Colours: White shirts with Black shorts
Telephone Nº: (0191) 478-3883
Daytime Phone Nº: (0191) 373-7014
Fax Number: (0191) 440-0404
Ground Capacity: 11,750
Seating Capacity: 11,750
Web site: www.gateshead-fc.com

GENERAL INFORMATION

Car Parking: At the stadium
Coach Parking: At the stadium
Nearest Railway Station: Gateshead Stadium Metro (½ mile); Newcastle (British Rail) 1½ miles
Nearest Bus Station: Heworth Interchange (½ mile)
Club Shop: At the stadium
Opening Times: Matchdays only
Telephone Nº: (0191) 478-3883

GROUND INFORMATION

Away Supporters' Entrances & Sections:
Tyne & Wear County Stand North End or the East Stand

ADMISSION INFO (2011/2012 PRICES)

Adult Seating: £14.00
Senior Citizen/Concessionary Seating: £9.00
Under-16s Seating: £2.00
Programme Price: £2.50

DISABLED INFORMATION

Wheelchairs: 5 spaces available each for home and away fans by the trackside – Level access with automatic doors
Helpers: Please phone the club for information
Prices: Please phone the club for information
Disabled Toilets: Available in the Reception Area and on the 1st floor concourse – accessible by lift.
Contact: (0191) 478-3883   (Bookings are necessary)

Travelling Supporters' Information:
Routes: From the South: Take the A1(M) to Washington Services and fork right onto the A194(M) signposted Tyne Tunnel. At the next roundabout, turn left onto the A184 signposted for Gateshead. The Stadium is on the right after 3 miles.

GRIMSBY TOWN FC

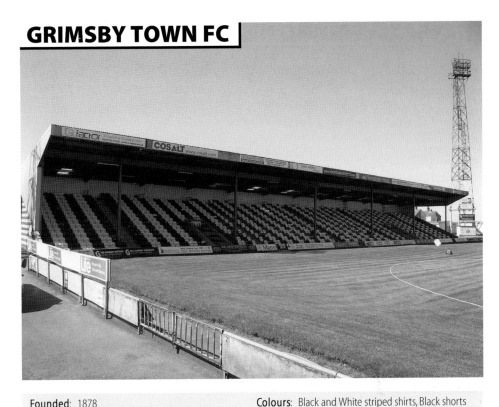

Founded: 1878
Former Names: Grimsby Pelham FC (1879)
Nickname: 'Mariners'
Ground: Blundell Park, Cleethorpes   DN35 7PY
Ground Capacity: 8,974 (All seats)
Record Attendance: 31,651 (20th February 1937)
Pitch Size: 111 × 74 yards

Colours: Black and White striped shirts, Black shorts
Telephone N°: (01472) 605050
Ticket Office: (01472) 605050
Fax Number: (01472) 693665
Web Site: www.gtfc.co.uk

GENERAL INFORMATION

Car Parking: Street parking
Coach Parking: Harrington Street – near the ground
Nearest Railway Station: Cleethorpes (1½ miles)
Nearest Bus Station: Brighowgate, Grimsby (4 miles)
Club Shop: At the ground
Opening Times: Monday – Friday 9.00am to 5.00pm; Matchday Saturdays 9.00am to kick-off
Telephone N°: (01472) 605050

GROUND INFORMATION

Away Supporters' Entrances & Sections:
Harrington Street turnstiles 15-18 and Constitution Avenue turnstiles 5-14

ADMISSION INFO (2011/2012 PRICES)

Adult Seating: £18.00 (Away fans £18.00)
Senior Citizens/Young Adults (Ages 15–18): £12.00
Child Seating: £8.00 (Under-15s)
Note: Tickets are cheaper if purchased before the matchday
Programme Price: £3.00

DISABLED INFORMATION

Wheelchairs: 50 spaces in total for Home and Away fans in the disabled section, in front of the Main Stand
Helpers: Helpers are admitted
Prices: £18.00 for the disabled. Free of charge for helpers
Disabled Toilets: Available in disabled section
Commentaries are available in disabled section
Contact: (01472) 605050 (Bookings are necessary)

Travelling Supporters' Information:
Routes: From All Parts except Lincolnshire and East Anglia: Take the M180 to the A180 and follow signs for Grimsby/Cleethorpes. The A180 ends at a roundabout (the 3rd in short distance after crossing docks), take the 2nd exit from the roundabout over the Railway flyover into Cleethorpes Road (A1098) and continue into Grimsby Road. After the second stretch of dual carriageway, the ground is ½ mile on the left; From Lincolnshire: Take the A46 or A16 and follow Cleethorpes signs along (A1098) Weelsby Road for 2 miles. Take the 1st exit at the roundabout at the end of Clee Road into Grimsby Road. The ground is 1¾ miles on the right.

HAYES & YEADING UNITED FC

Hayes & Yeading United FC are groundsharing with Woking FC for the 2011/2012 season.

Founded: 2007
Former Names: Formed by the amalgamation of Hayes FC and Yeading FC in 2007
Nickname: 'United'
Ground: Kingfield Stadium, Kingfield, Woking, Surrey   GU22 9AA
Record Attendance: 6,000 (1997)
Pitch Size: 109 × 76 yards

Colours: Red Shirts with Black shorts
Telephone Nº: (020) 8756-1200
Fax Number: (020) 8756-1200
Ground Capacity: 6,161
Seating Capacity: 2,511
Web site: www.hyufc.net

GENERAL INFORMATION
Car Parking: Limited parking at the ground
Coach Parking: At or opposite the ground
Nearest Railway Station: Woking (1 mile)
Nearest Bus Station: Woking
Club Shop: None

GROUND INFORMATION
Away Supporters' Entrances & Sections:
Kingfield Road entrance for the Tennis Club terrace

ADMISSION INFO (2011/2012 PRICES)
Adult Standing: £12.00
Adult Seating: £12.00
Under-16s/Student Standing: £2.00
Under-16s/Student Seating: £2.00
Senior Citizen Standing: £8.00
Senior Citizen Seating: £8.00
Programme Price: £2.50

DISABLED INFORMATION
Wheelchairs: 8 spaces in the Leslie Gosden Stand and 8 spaces in front of the Family Stand
Helpers: Admitted
Prices: One wheelchair and helper for £8.00
Disabled Toilets: Yes – in the Leslie Gosden Stand and Family Stand area
Contact: (020) 8756-1200   (Bookings are necessary)

Travelling Supporters' Information:
Routes: Exit the M25 at Junction 10 and follow the A3 towards Guildford. Leave at the next junction onto the B2215 through Ripley and join the A247 to Woking. Alternatively, exit the M25 at Junction 11 and follow the A320 to Woking Town Centre. The ground is on the outskirts of Woking – follow signs on the A320 and A247.

KETTERING TOWN FC

Founded: 1872
Former Names: Kettering FC
Nickname: 'The Poppies'
Ground: Nene Park, Diamond Way, Irthlingborough, Northants NN9 5QF
Record Attendance: 11,526 (at Rockingham Road)
Pitch Size: 111 × 74 yards

Colours: Red shirts with Black shorts and socks
Telephone Nº: (01536) 483028
Daytime Phone Nº: (01536) 517013
Fax Number: (01536) 412273
Ground Capacity: 6,441
Seating Capacity: 4,641
Web site: www.ketteringtownfc.co.uk

GENERAL INFORMATION

Car Parking: At the ground (£3.00 charge)
Coach Parking: At the ground (£10.00 charge)
Nearest Railway Station: Wellingborough (5 miles)
Nearest Bus Station: Wellingborough
Club Shop: Yes – at the front of the Stadium
Opening Times: Check web site for further details
Telephone Nº: –

GROUND INFORMATION

Away Supporters' Entrances & Sections:
Please phone the club for further information

ADMISSION INFO (2011/2012 PRICES)

Adult Standing: £15.00
Adult Seating: £16.00
Concessionary Standing: £12.00
Concessionary Seating: £13.00
Under-16s Standing/Seating: £3.00
Note: The above prices may change during the season
Programme Price: £3.00

DISABLED INFORMATION

Wheelchairs: Accommodated around the ground
Helpers: Admitted
Prices: Normal prices apply for the disabled fans with registered carers admitted free of charge
Disabled Toilets: Available around the ground
Contact: (01933) 652936 Matt Banyard

Travelling Supporters' Information:
Routes: The ground is located on the A6 about 350 yards north of the junction with the A45 (over the bridge). This is approximately 6 miles south of the A14.

19

KIDDERMINSTER HARRIERS FC

Founded: 1886
Nickname: 'Harriers'
Ground: Aggborough, Hoo Road, Kidderminster, Worcestershire DY10 1NB
Ground Capacity: 6,444
Seating Capacity: 3,143
Record Attendance: 9,155 (1948)

Pitch Size: 110 × 72 yards
Colours: Red shirts and shorts
Telephone Nº: (01562) 823931
Fax Number: (01562) 827329
Web Site: www.harriers.co.uk

GENERAL INFORMATION
Car Parking: At the ground
Coach Parking: As directed
Nearest Railway Station: Kidderminster
Nearest Bus Station: Kidderminster Town Centre
Club Shop: At the ground
Opening Times: Weekdays and First Team Matchdays 9.00am to 5.00pm
Telephone Nº: (01562) 823931

GROUND INFORMATION
Away Supporters' Entrances & Sections:
John Smiths Stand Entrance D and South Terrace Entrance E

ADMISSION INFO (2011/2012 PRICES)
Adult Standing: £14.00
Adult Seating: £17.00
Senior Citizen Standing: £8.00   Under-16s: £5.00
Senior Citizen Seating: £11.00   Under-16s: £8.00
Note: Under-8s are admitted free with a paying adult
Programme Price: £2.50

DISABLED INFORMATION
Wheelchairs: Home fans accommodated at the front of the Main Stand, Away fans in front of the John Smiths Stand
Helpers: Admitted
Prices: £10.00 for each disabled fan plus one helper
Disabled Toilets: Available by the disabled area
Contact: (01562) 823931   (Bookings are not necessary)

Travelling Supporters' Information:
Routes: Exit the M5 at Junction 3 and follow the A456 to Kidderminster. The ground is situated close by the Severn Valley Railway Station so follow the brown Steam Train signs and turn into Hoo Road about 200 yards downhill of the station. Follow the road along for ¼ mile and the ground is on the left.

LINCOLN CITY FC

Founded: 1884
Nickname: 'Red Imps'
Ground: Sincil Bank Stadium, Lincoln   LN5 8LD
Ground Capacity: 10,120 (All seats)
Record Attendance: 23,196 (15th November 1967)
Pitch Size: 110 × 72 yards

Colours: Red and White striped shirts, Black shorts
Telephone Nº: (01522) 880011
Ticket Office: (01522) 880011
Fax Number: (01522) 880020
Web Site: www.redimps.com

GENERAL INFORMATION

Car Parking: Stacey West Car Park (limited parking for £5.00 per car).
Coach Parking: Please contact the club for details.
Nearest Railway Station: Lincoln Central
Club Shop: At the ground
Opening Times: Weekdays 9.00am to 5.00pm and Saturday Matchdays 10.00am to 5.00pm
Telephone Nº: (01522) 880011

GROUND INFORMATION

Away Supporters' Entrances & Sections:
Lincolnshire Co-operative Stand (seated) – Turnstiles 19-23

ADMISSION INFO (2011/2012 PRICES)

Adult Seating: £14.00 – £18.00
Child Seating: £6.00 – £7.00
Concessionary Seating: £10.00 – £13.00
Note: Prices vary depending on the category of the game and area of the ground and discounts are available for advance ticket purchases
Programme Price: £2.50

DISABLED INFORMATION

Wheelchairs: Limited number of spaces available in the disabled section, adjacent to turnstile 23
Helpers: One helper admitted per disabled person
Prices: Applications for disabled passes must be made to the club. Wheelchair-bound disabled are charged concessionary prices. Helpers are admitted free if the disabled fan has a medium/high level disability allowance
Disabled Toilets: Adjacent to disabled area
Contact: (01522) 880011   (Bookings are necessary)

Travelling Supporters' Information:
Routes: From the East: Take the A46 or A158 into the City Centre following Newark (A46) signs into the High Street and take next left (Scorer Street and Cross Street) for the ground; From the North and West: Take the A15 or A57 into the City Centre, then as from the East; From the South: Take the A1 then A46 for the City Centre, then into the High Street, parking on the South Common or in the Stadium via South Park Avenue, turn down by the Fire Station.

LUTON TOWN FC

Founded: 1885
Former Names: The club was formed by the amalgamation of Wanderers FC and Excelsior FC
Nickname: 'Hatters'
Ground: Kenilworth Road Stadium, 1 Maple Road, Luton LU4 8AW
Ground Capacity: 10,226 (All seats)
Record Attendance: 30,069 (4th March 1959)

Pitch Size: 110 × 72 yards
Colours: Orange shirts with Blue shorts
Telephone N°: (01582) 411622
Ticket Office: (01582) 416976
Fax Number: (01582) 405070
Web Site: www.lutontown.co.uk

GENERAL INFORMATION

Car Parking: Street parking
Coach Parking: Luton Bus Station
Nearest Railway Station: Luton (1 mile)
Nearest Bus Station: Bute Street, Luton
Club Shop: Kenilworth Road Forecourt
Opening Times: 10.00am to 4.00pm
Telephone N°: (01582) 411622

GROUND INFORMATION

Away Supporters' Entrances & Sections:
Oak Road for the Oak Stand

ADMISSION INFO (2011/2012 PRICES)

Adult Seating: £15.00 – £18.00
Under-10s Seating: £5.00
Under-17s Seating: £8.00
Under-22s Seating: £13.00
Senior Citizen Seating: £10.00 – £13.00
Note: Tickets are cheaper if bought prior to the matchday
Programme Price: £3.00

DISABLED INFORMATION

Wheelchairs: 32 spaces in total for Home and Away fans in the disabled section, Kenilworth Road End and Main Stand
Helpers: One helper admitted per disabled person
Prices: £15.00 for the disabled. Free of charge for helpers
Disabled Toilets: Available adjacent to disabled area
Commentaries are available for the blind
Contact: (01582) 416976 (Bookings are necessary)

Travelling Supporters' Information:
Routes: From the North and West: Exit the M1 at Junction 11 and follow signs for Luton (A505) into Dunstable Road. Follow the one-way system and turn right back towards Dunstable, take the second left into Ash Road for the ground; From the South and East: Exit the M1 at Junction 10 (or A6/A612) into Luton Town Centre and follow signs into Dunstable Road. After the railway bridge, take the sixth turning on the left into Ash Road for the ground.

MANSFIELD TOWN FC

Founded: 1897
Former Name: Mansfield Wesleyans FC (1897-1905)
Nickname: 'Stags'
Ground: Field Mill Ground, Quarry Lane, Mansfield, Nottinghamshire   NG18 5DA
Ground Capacity: 10,000 (All seats)
Record Attendance: 24,467 (10th January 1953)
Pitch Size: 114 × 70 yards

Colours: Amber shirts with Royal Blue piping, Royal Blue shorts with Amber flash
Telephone Nº: (01623) 482483
Ticket Office: (01623) 482483
Fax Number: (01623) 482495
Web Site: www.mansfieldtown.net
E-mail: info@mansfieldtown.net

GENERAL INFORMATION

Car Parking: Large car park at the ground (£2.50)
Coach Parking: Adjacent to the ground
Nearest Railway Station: Mansfield (5 minutes walk)
Nearest Bus Station: Mansfield
Club Shop: In the South Stand of the Stadium
Opening Times: Weekdays 9.00am – 5.00pm and Matchdays 10.00am – 3.00pm
Telephone Nº: (0870) 756-3160

GROUND INFORMATION

Away Supporters' Entrances & Sections:
North Stand turnstiles for North Stand seating

ADMISSION INFO (2011/2012 PRICES)

Adult Seating: £15.00 – £18.00
Senior Citizen Seating: £12.00
Junior Seating: £7.00 – £9.00
Under-7s Seating: £2.00
Programme Price: £2.50

DISABLED INFORMATION

Wheelchairs: 90 spaces available in total in the disabled sections in the North Stand, Quarry Street Stand & West Stand
Helpers: Admitted
Prices: £8.00 for the disabled. Helpers £15.00
Disabled Toilets: Available in the North Stand, West Stand and Quarry Lane Stand
Contact: (0870) 756-3160 (Please buy tickets in advance)

Travelling Supporters' Information:
Routes: From the North: Exit the M1 at Junction 29 and take the A617 to Mansfield. After 6¼ miles turn right at the Leisure Centre into Rosemary Street. Carry on to Quarry Lane and turn right; From the South and West: Exit the M1 at Junction 28 and take the A38 to Mansfield. After 6½ miles turn right at the crossroads into Belvedere Street then turn right after ¼ mile into Quarry Lane; From the East: Take the A617 to Rainworth, turn left at the crossroads after 3 miles into Windsor Road and turn right at the end into Nottingham Road, then left into Quarry Lane.

NEWPORT COUNTY AFC

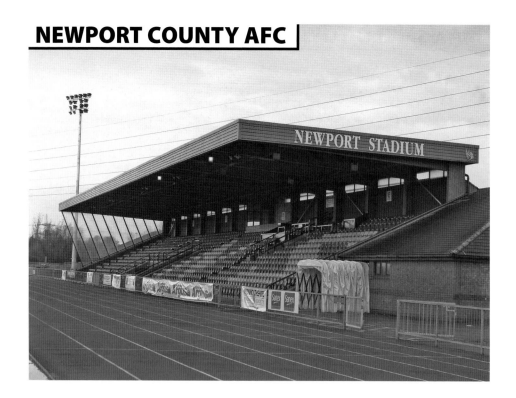

Founded: 1989
Former Names: Newport AFC
Nickname: 'The Exiles'
Ground: Newport Stadium, Stadium Way, Newport International Sports Village, Newport NP19 4PT
Record Attendance: 4,616 (11th November 2006)
Pitch Size: 112 × 72 yards

Colours: Amber shirts with Black shorts
Telephone Nº: (01633) 662262
Fax Number: (01633) 666107
Ground Capacity: 4,300
Seating Capacity: 1,236
Web site: www.newport-county.co.uk

GENERAL INFORMATION

Car Parking: Space for 500 cars at the ground
Coach Parking: At the ground
Nearest Railway Station: Newport
Nearest Bus Station: Newport
Club Shop: At the ground
Opening Times: Matchdays only
Telephone Nº: (01633) 662262

GROUND INFORMATION

Away Supporters' Entrances & Sections:
No segregation unless specifically required by the Police

ADMISSION INFO (2011/2012 PRICES)

Adult Standing: £14.00   Adult Seating: £15.00
Senior Citizen Standing: £10.00
Senior Citizen Seating: £11.00
Full-time Student Standing: £10.00
Full-time Student Seating: £11.00
Under-16s Standing: £5.00   Under-16s Seating: £8.00
Note: Under-5s are admitted free of charge
Programme Price: £2.80

DISABLED INFORMATION

Wheelchairs: Accommodated
Helpers: Admitted
Prices: Normal prices for the disabled. Free for helpers
Disabled Toilets: Yes
Contact: (01633) 662262   (Bookings are not necessary)

Travelling Supporters' Information:
Routes: Exit the M4 at Junction 24 and take the A48 exit at the roundabout, signposted 'Newport Int. Sports Village'. Go straight on at the first two roundabouts then bear left at the 3rd roundabout. Carry straight on over the next two roundabouts, then turn left before the Carcraft site. Take the 1st turning on the left into the Stadium car park.

SOUTHPORT FC

Founded: 1881
Former Names: Southport Vulcan FC, Southport Central FC
Nickname: 'The Sandgrounders'
Ground: Haig Avenue, Southport, Merseyside, PR8 6JZ
Record Attendance: 20,010 (1932)
Pitch Size: 110 × 77 yards

Colours: Yellow shirts and shorts
Telephone Nº: (01704) 533422
Fax Number: (01704) 533455
Ground Capacity: 6,001
Seating Capacity: 1,640
Web site: www.southportfc.net

GENERAL INFORMATION

Car Parking: Street parking
Coach Parking: Adjacent to the ground
Nearest Railway Station: Southport (1½ miles)
Nearest Bus Station: Southport Town Centre
Club Shop: At the ground
Opening Times: Matchdays from 1.30pm (from 6.30pm on evening matchdays)
Telephone Nº: (01704) 533422

GROUND INFORMATION

Away Supporters' Entrances & Sections:
Blowick End entrances

ADMISSION INFO (2011/2012 PRICES)

Adult Standing: £12.50
Adult Seating: £14.00
Child/Senior Citizen Standing: £9.00
Child/Senior Citizen Seating: £10.00
Programme Price: £2.50

DISABLED INFORMATION

Wheelchairs: Accommodated in front of the Grandstand
Helpers: Admitted
Prices: Concessionary prices charged for the disabled. Helpers are admitted free of charge
Disabled Toilets: Available at the Blowick End of the Grandstand
Contact: (01704) 533422   (Bookings are not necessary)

Travelling Supporters' Information:
Routes: Exit the M58 at Junction 3 and take the A570 to Southport. At the major roundabout (McDonalds/Tesco) go straight on into Scarisbrick New Road, pass over the brook and turn right into Haig Avenue at the traffic lights. The ground is then on the right-hand side.

STOCKPORT COUNTY FC

Founded: 1883
Former Names: Heaton Norris Rovers FC
Nickname: 'Hatters' 'County'
Ground: Edgeley Park, Hardcastle Road, Edgeley, Stockport SK3 9DD
Ground Capacity: 10,641 (All seats)
Record Attendance: 27,833 (11th February 1950)
Pitch Size: 111 × 72 yards

Colours: Blue and White striped shirts, Blue shorts
Telephone Nº: (0161) 286-8903
Ticket Office: 0845 688-5799
Fax Number: (0161) 429-7392
Web Site: www.stockportcounty.com

GENERAL INFORMATION
Car Parking: Booth Street (nearby) £4.00
Coach Parking: Booth Street (£20.00)
Nearest Railway Station: Stockport (5 minutes walk)
Nearest Bus Station: Mersey Square (10 minutes walk)
Club Shop: At the ground
Opening Times: Weekdays 9.30am – 5.00pm. Open until 7.30pm on matchdays during the week and also on Saturday matchdays 10.00am – 2.45pm then for 30 minutes after the game.
Telephone Nº: (0161) 286-8888

GROUND INFORMATION
Away Supporters' Entrances & Sections:
Railway End turnstiles for Railway End or turnstiles for Popular Side depending on the opponents

ADMISSION INFO (2011/2012 PRICES)
Adult Seating: £18.00
Under-22s Seating: £11.00
Under-17s Seating: £3.00
Under-7s Seating: Free of charge
Senior Citizen Seating: £11.00
Programme Price: £3.00

DISABLED INFORMATION
Wheelchairs: 16 spaces in total. 10 in the Hardcastle Road Stand, 6 in the Cheadle Stand
Helpers: One helper admitted per disabled fan
Prices: £11.00 for the disabled. Helpers free of charge
Disabled Toilets: Yes
Contact: (0161) 286-8888 (Bookings are necessary)

Travelling Supporters' Information:
Routes: From the North, South and West: Exit the M63 at Junction 11 and join the A560, following signs for Cheadle. After ¼ mile turn right into Edgeley Road and after 1 mile turn right into Caroline Street for the ground; From the East: Take the A6 or A560 into Stockport Town Centre and turn left into Greek Street. Take the 2nd exit into Mercian Way (from the roundabout) then turn left into Caroline Street – the ground is straight ahead.

TAMWORTH FC

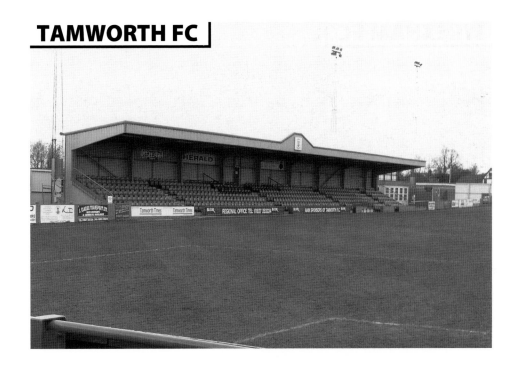

Founded: 1933
Former Names: None
Nickname: 'The Lambs'
Ground: The Lamb Ground, Kettlebrook, Tamworth, B77 1AA
Record Attendance: 4,920 (3rd April 1948)
Pitch Size: 110 × 73 yards

Colours: Red shirts with Black shorts
Telephone Nº: (01827) 65798
Fax Number: (01827) 62236
Ground Capacity: 4,118
Seating Capacity: 520
Web site: www.thelambs.co.uk

GENERAL INFORMATION

Car Parking: 200 spaces available at the ground – £2.00 per car, £5.00 for per minibus or £10.00 per coach
Coach Parking: At the ground
Nearest Railway Station: Tamworth (½ mile)
Nearest Bus Station: Tamworth (½ mile)
Club Shop: At the ground
Opening Times: Weekdays from 10.00am to 4.00pm and also on Matchdays
Telephone Nº: (01827) 65798

GROUND INFORMATION

Away Supporters' Entrances & Sections:
Gates 1 and 2 for Terracing, Gate 2A for seating

ADMISSION INFO (2011/2012 PRICES)

Adult Standing: £10.00 – £14.00
Adult Seating: £12.00 – £16.00
Child Standing: £1.00
Child Seating: £3.00
Senior Citizen Standing: £9.00
Senior Citizen Seating: £11.00
Note: Prices vary depending on the category of the game
Programme Price: £2.50

DISABLED INFORMATION

Wheelchairs: Accommodated
Helpers: Admitted
Prices: Normal prices apply for Wheelchair disabled. Helpers are charged concessionary rates
Disabled Toilets: Yes
Contact: (01827) 65798 (Bookings are advisable)

Travelling Supporters' Information:
Routes: Exit the M42 at Junction 10 and take the A5/A51 to the town centre following signs for Town Centre/Snowdome. The follow signs for Kettlebrook and the ground is in Kettlebrook Road, 50 yards from the traffic island by the Railway Viaduct and the Snowdome. The ground is signposted from all major roads.

WREXHAM FC

Founded: 1872
Nickname: 'Red Dragons'
Ground: Racecourse Ground, Mold Road, Wrexham, North Wales LL11 2AH
Ground Capacity: 10,500 (all seats) at present as the ground undergoes re-development
Record Attendance: 34,445 (26th January 1957)

Pitch Size: 111 × 71 yards
Colours: Red shirts with White shorts
Telephone Nº: (01978) 262129
Fax Number: (01978) 357821
Web Site: www.wrexhamafc.co.uk

GENERAL INFORMATION
Car Parking: Town car parks are nearby and also Glyndwr University (Mold End)
Coach Parking: By Police direction
Nearest Railway Station: Wrexham General (adjacent)
Nearest Bus Station: Wrexham (King Street)
Club Shop: At the ground in the Yale Stand
Opening Times: Monday to Saturday 9.00am to 5.00pm
Telephone Nº: (01978) 262129

GROUND INFORMATION
Away Supporters' Entrances & Sections:
Turnstiles 1-4 for the Yale Stand

ADMISSION INFO (2011/2012 PRICES)
Adult Seating: £17.00 – £20.00
Child Seating: £5.00 – £10.00
Under-7s Seating: Free with a paying adult.
Senior Citizen Seating: £10.00 – £12.00
Note: Tickets are cheaper when purchased in advance
Programme Price: £3.00

DISABLED INFORMATION
Wheelchairs: 35 spaces in the Mold Road Stand
Helpers: One helper admitted per wheelchair
Prices: £10.00 for the disabled. Free of charge for helpers
Disabled Toilets: Available in the disabled section
Contact: (01978) 262129 (Bookings are preferred)

Travelling Supporters' Information:
Routes: From the North and West: Take the A483 and the Wrexham bypass to the junction with the A541. Branch left at the roundabout and follow Wrexham signs into Mold Road; From the East: Take the A525 or A534 into Wrexham then follow the A541 signs into Mold Road; From the South: Take the the M6, then the M54 and follow the A5 and A483 to the Wrexham bypass and the junction with the A541. Branch right at the roundabout and follow signs for the Town Centre.

YORK CITY FC

Founded: 1922
Nickname: 'Minstermen'
Ground: Bootham Crescent, York   YO30 7AQ
Ground Capacity: 8,105
Seating Capacity: 3,509
Record Attendance: 28,123 (5th March 1938)
Pitch Size: 115 × 74 yards

Colours: Red shirts with Blue shorts
Telephone Nº: (01904) 624447
Ticket Office: (01904) 624447 Extension 1
Fax Number: (01904) 631457 or 08712 515800
Web Site: www.ycfc.net

GENERAL INFORMATION

Car Parking: Street parking
Coach Parking: By Police direction
Nearest Railway Station: York (1 mile)
Nearest Bus Station: York
Club Shop: At the ground
Opening Times: Weekdays 10.30am – 2.30pm and
Saturday Matchdays 1.00pm–3.00pm and 4.40pm–5.30pm;
Evening matches open from 6.00pm
Telephone Nº: (01904) 624447 Extension 4

GROUND INFORMATION

Away Supporters' Entrances & Sections:
Grosvenor Road turnstiles for Grosvenor Road End

ADMISSION INFO (2011/2012 PRICES)

Adult Standing: £15.00
Adult Seating: £16.00 – £18.00
Concessionary Standing: £10.00
Concessionary Seating: £10.00 – £12.00
Under-16s Standing/Seating: £6.00 – £7.00
Programme Price: £3.00

DISABLED INFORMATION

Wheelchairs: 18 spaces in total for Home and Away fans in
the disabled section, in front of the Pitchside Bar
Helpers: One helper admitted per disabled person
Prices: £16.00 for the disabled. Free of charge for helpers
Disabled Toilets: Available at entrance to the disabled area
Contact: (01904) 624447 (Ext. 1) (Bookings not necessary)

Travelling Supporters' Information:
Routes: From the North: Take the A1 then the A59 following signs for York. Cross the railway bridge and turn left after 2 miles
into Water End. Turn right at the end following City Centre signs for nearly ½ mile then turn left into Bootham Crescent; From
the South: Take the A64 and turn left after Buckles Inn onto the Outer Ring Road. Turn right onto the A19, follow City Centre
signs for 1½ miles then turn left into Bootham Crescent; From the East: Take the Outer Ring Road turning left onto the A19.
Then as from the South; From the West: Take the Outer Ring Road turning right onto the A19. Then as from the South.

THE FOOTBALL CONFERENCE BLUE SQUARE NORTH

Address

Third Floor, Wellington House,
31-34 Waterloo Street, Birmingham   B2 5TJ

Phone (0121) 214-1950

Web site www.footballconference.co.uk

Clubs for the 2011/2012 Season

ALTRINCHAM FC

Founded: 1891
Former Names: Broadheath FC
Nickname: 'The Robins'
Ground: Moss Lane, Altrincham   WA15 8AP
Record Attendance: 10,275 (February 1925)
Pitch Size: 110 × 72 yards

Colours: Red and White striped shirts, Black shorts
Telephone Nº: (0161) 928-1045
Daytime Phone Nº: (0161) 928-1045
Fax Number: (0161) 926-9934
Ground Capacity: 6,085
Seating Capacity: 1,154
Web site: www.altrinchamfc.com

GENERAL INFORMATION

Car Parking: Limited street parking
Coach Parking: By Police Direction
Nearest Railway Station: Altrincham (5 minutes walk)
Nearest Bus Station: Altrincham
Club Shop: Inside the ground
Opening Times: Matchdays only. Opens one hour prior to the start of the game.
Telephone Nº: (0161) 928-1045

GROUND INFORMATION

Away Supporters' Entrances & Sections:
Hale End turnstiles and accommodation

ADMISSION INFO (2011/2012 PRICES)

Adult Standing: £13.00
Adult Seating: £15.00
Concessionary Standing: £8.00
Concessionary Seating: £9.00
Ages 12-16 years Standing/Seating: £5.00
Under-12s Standing/Seating: £2.00
Programme Price: £2.00

DISABLED INFORMATION

Wheelchairs: 3 spaces are available each for home and away fans adjacent to the Away dugout
Helpers: Admitted
Prices: Free for the disabled. £13.00 for helpers
Disabled Toilets: Yes
Contact: (0161) 928-1045   (Bookings are necessary)

Travelling Supporters' Information:
Routes: Exit the M56 at either Junction 6 or 7 and follow the signs for Altrincham FC.

BISHOP'S STORTFORD FC

Founded: 1874
Former Names: None
Nickname: 'Blues' 'Bishops'
Ground: Woodside Park, Dunmow Road,
Bishop's Stortford CM23 5RG
Record Attendance: 3,555 (2000)
Pitch Size: 110 × 70 yards

Colours: Blue and White shirts with Blue shorts
Telephone Nº: (01279) 306456
Fax Number: (01279) 715621
Ground Capacity: 4,000
Seating Capacity: 500
Web site: www.bsfc.co.uk

GENERAL INFORMATION

Car Parking: 500 spaces available at the ground
Coach Parking: At the ground
Nearest Railway Station: Bishop's Stortford
Nearest Bus Station: Bishop's Stortford
Club Shop: At the ground
Opening Times: Matchdays only 1.30pm to 5.00pm
Telephone Nº: (01279) 306456

GROUND INFORMATION

Away Supporters' Entrances & Sections:
No usual segregation

ADMISSION INFO (2011/2012 PRICES)

Adult Standing/Seating: £12.00
Concessionary Standing/Seating: £7.00
Student Standing/Seating: £6.00
Under-16s Standing/Seating: £5.00
Note: Under-12s are admitted free of charge when
accompanied by a paying adult.
Programme Price: £2.50

DISABLED INFORMATION

Wheelchairs: Accommodated in the disabled section
Helpers: Admitted
Prices: Free of charge for the disabled and helpers
Disabled Toilets: Yes
Contact: (01279) 306456   (Bookings are not necessary)

Travelling Supporters' Information:
Routes: Exit the M11 at junction 8 and take the A1250 towards Bishop Stortford. Turn left at the first roundabout and the ground is first right opposite the Golf Club (the entrance is between Industrial Units).

BLYTH SPARTANS FC

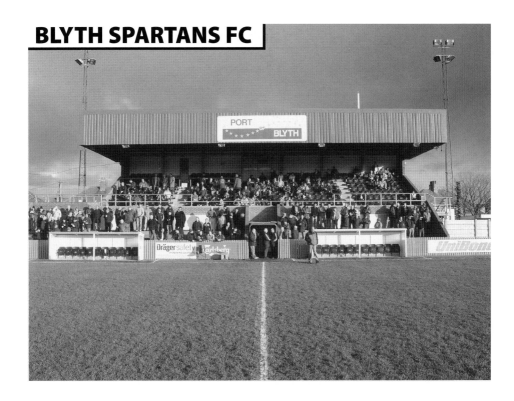

Founded: 1899
Former Names: None
Nickname: 'Spartans'
Ground: Croft Park, Blyth, Northumberland, NE24 3JE
Record Attendance: 10,186
Pitch Size: 110 × 70 yards

Colours: Green and White striped shirts, Black shorts
Telephone Nº: (01670) 352373 (Office)
Fax Number: (01670) 545592
Ground Capacity: 6,000
Seating Capacity: 540
Web site: www.blythspartansafc.co.uk

GENERAL INFORMATION

Car Parking: At the ground
Coach Parking: At the ground
Nearest Railway Station: Newcastle
Nearest Bus Station: Blyth (5 minutes walk)
Club Shop: At the ground
Opening Times: Matchdays only
Telephone Nº: c/o (01670) 336379

GROUND INFORMATION

Away Supporters' Entrances & Sections:
No usual segregation

ADMISSION INFO (2011/2012 PRICES)

Adult Standing: £10.00
Adult Seating: £11.50
Concessionary Standing: £5.50
Concessionary Seating: £6.50
Note: Under-10s are admitted free of charge when accompanied by a paying adult
Programme Price: £2.00

DISABLED INFORMATION

Wheelchairs: Accommodated
Helpers: Please phone the club for information
Prices: Please phone the club for information
Disabled Toilets: Yes
Contact: (01670) 352373 (Bookings are necessary)

Travelling Supporters' Information:
Routes: Pass through the Tyne Tunnel and take the left lane for Morpeth (A19/A1). At the 2nd roundabout (after approximately 7 miles) take full right turn for the A189 (signposted Ashington). After 2 miles take the slip road (A1061 signposted Blyth). Follow signs for Blyth turning left at the caravan site. At the 2nd roundabout turn right and the ground is on the left.

BOSTON UNITED FC

Founded: 1933	**Record Attendance**: 10,086 (1955)
Former Names: Boston Town FC & Boston Swifts FC	**Colours**: Amber and Black shirts, Black shorts
Nickname: 'The Pilgrims'	**Telephone Nº**: (01205) 364406 (Office)
Ground: Jakeman's Stadium, York Street, Boston, PE21 6JN	**Matchday Info**: (01205) 364406 or 07860 663299
	Fax Number: (01205) 354063
Ground Capacity: 6,613 **Seating Capacity**: 2,000	**Web Site**: www.bufc.co.uk
Pitch Size: 112 × 72 yards	**E-mail**: admin@bufc.co.uk

GENERAL INFORMATION

Car Parking: Permit holders only
Coach Parking: Available near to the ground
Nearest Railway Station: Boston (1 mile)
Nearest Bus Station: Boston Coach Station (¼ mile)
Club Shop: In the car park at the ground
Opening Times: Weekdays from 9.00am to 5.00pm and Saturday Matchdays from 11.00am to 5.00pm
Telephone Nº: (01205) 364406

GROUND INFORMATION

Away Supporters' Entrances & Sections:
York Street Entrances 3 & 4 (subject to a move to the Jakemans Stand if so advised by the police)

ADMISSION INFO (2011/2012 PRICES)

Adult Standing: £12.00
Adult Seating: £14.00
Child Standing: £4.00
Child Seating: £5.00
Senior Citizen Standing: £9.00
Senior Citizen Seating: £10.00
Programme Price: £2.50

DISABLED INFORMATION

Wheelchairs: 7 spaces available for home fans, 4 spaces for away fans below the Main Stand at the Town End
Helpers: One helper admitted per disabled fan
Prices: £12.00 for the disabled. Free of charge for helpers
Disabled Toilets: Available in the Town End Terrace
Contact: (01205) 364406 (Bookings are necessary)

Travelling Supporters' Information:
From the North: Take the A17 from Sleaford, bear right after the railway crossing to the traffic lights over the bridge. Go forward through the traffic lights into York Street for the ground; From the South: Take the A16 from Spalding and turn right at the traffic lights over the bridge. Go forward through the next traffic lights into York Street for the ground.

COLWYN BAY FC

Founded: 1885
Former Names: None
Nickname: 'Bay' 'Seagulls'
Ground: Llanelian Road, Old Colwyn, Colwyn Bay, LL29 8UN
Record Attendance: 2,500

Colours: Sky Blue shirts and shorts
Telephone Nº: (01492) 514680
Ground Capacity: 2,500
Seating Capacity: 403
Web site: www.colwynbayfc.co.uk

GENERAL INFORMATION

Car Parking: At the ground
Coach Parking: At the ground
Nearest Railway Station: Colwyn Bay (1 mile)
Nearest Bus Station: Colwyn Bay
Club Shop: At the ground
Opening Times: Matchdays only
Telephone Nº: (01422) 341222

GROUND INFORMATION

Away Supporters' Entrances & Sections:
No usual segregation

ADMISSION INFO (2011/2012 PRICES)

Adult Standing/Seating: £9.00
Concessionary Standing/Seating: £5.00
Student Standing/Seating: £5.00
Under-14s Standing/Seating: £2.00
Programme Price: £2.50

DISABLED INFORMATION

Wheelchairs: Accommodated in Covered Terrace
Helpers: Admitted
Prices: Please phone the club for information
Disabled Toilets: Available in the Social Club
Contact: (01492) 514581 (Bookings are not necessary)

Travelling Supporters' Information:
Routes: From Queensferry: Take the A55 and when the expressway is reached take Junction 22 (signposted Old Colwyn). Turn left at the bottom of the slip road then straight on at the mini-roundabout into Llanelian Road. The ground is ½ mile on the right.

CORBY TOWN FC

Photograph courtesy of Chris Rivett, Final Third Sports Media

Founded: 1948
Former Names: None
Nickname: 'The Steelmen'
Ground: Rockingham Triangle Stadium, Rockingham Road, Corby   NN17 2AE
Record Attendance: 2,240 vs Watford (1986/87)
Pitch Size: 109 × 70 yards

Colours: White shirts with Black shorts
Telephone Nº: (01536) 406640
Fax Number: (0116) 237-6162
Ground Capacity: 3,893
Seating Capacity: 577
Web site: www.corbytownfc.co.uk

GENERAL INFORMATION

Car Parking: Spaces for 190 cars at the ground
Coach Parking: Spaces for 3 coaches at the ground
Nearest Railway Station: Corby (2 miles)
Nearest Bus Station: Corby Town Centre
Club Shop: At the ground
Opening Times: Matchdays only – 1 hour before kick-off
Telephone Nº: (01536) 406640

GROUND INFORMATION

Away Supporters' Entrances & Sections:
No usual segregation

ADMISSION INFO (2011/2012 PRICES)

Adult Standing/Seating: £11.00
Under-16s Standing/Seating: £2.00
Senior Citizen Standing/Seating: £7.00
Note: Family tickets are also available, costing £20.00
Programme Price: £2.00

DISABLED INFORMATION

Wheelchairs: Accommodated
Helpers: Admitted
Prices: Normal prices apply for disabled fans. Helpers are admitted free of charge
Disabled Toilets: Available
Contact: (01536) 406640   (Bookings are not necessary)

Travelling Supporters' Information:
Routes: From the North & East: Exit the A1(M) at junction 17 and take the A605 to Oundle then the A427 to Little Weldon. At the roundabout take the A6116 towards Rockingham and the ground is adjacent to Rockingham Castle near the junction with the A6003; From the South: Take the A14 to the junction with the A6116 and continue to the junction with the A6003 at Rockingham Castle; From the West: Take the A14 or A427 to the A6003 then continue north towards Rockingham to the junction with the A6116 where the ground is on the left.

DROYLSDEN FC

Founded: 1892	**Colours**: Red shirts with Red shorts
Former Names: None	**Telephone Nº**: (0161) 370-1426
Nickname: 'The Bloods'	**Daytime Phone Nº**: (0161) 370-1426
Ground: Butchers Arms, Market Street, Droylsden, Manchester M43 7AY	**Fax Number**: (0161) 370-8341
	Ground Capacity: 3,500
Record Attendance: 5,400 (1973)	**Seating Capacity**: 500
Pitch Size: 110 × 70 yards	**Web site**: www.droylsdenfc.com

GENERAL INFORMATION

Car Parking: Street parking only
Coach Parking: At the ground
Nearest Railway Station: Manchester Piccadilly
Nearest Bus Station: Ashton
Club Shop: At the ground
Opening Times: Matchdays only
Telephone Nº: (0161) 370-1426

GROUND INFORMATION

Away Supporters' Entrances & Sections:
No usual segregation

ADMISSION INFO (2011/2012 PRICES)

Adult Standing: £10.00
Adult Seating: £10.00
Concessionary Standing: £6.00
Concessionary Seating: £6.00
Note: Under-14s are admitted free of charge when accompanied by a paying adult
Programme Price: £2.00

DISABLED INFORMATION

Wheelchairs: Accommodated beside the Stand
Helpers: Yes
Prices: Normal prices apply for the disabled and helpers
Disabled Toilets: Available
Contact: (0161) 370-1426   (Bookings are not necessary)

Travelling Supporters' Information:
Routes: Take the Manchester Outer Ring Road M60 and exit at Junction 23. Join the A635 towards Manchester and after the retail park on the left, take the centre lane, then turn right at the traffic lights onto the A662 signposted for Droylsden. At the next traffic lights, turn right onto Market Street and after 150 yards go straight on at the traffic lights. The entrance to the ground is 75 yards on the left.

EASTWOOD TOWN FC

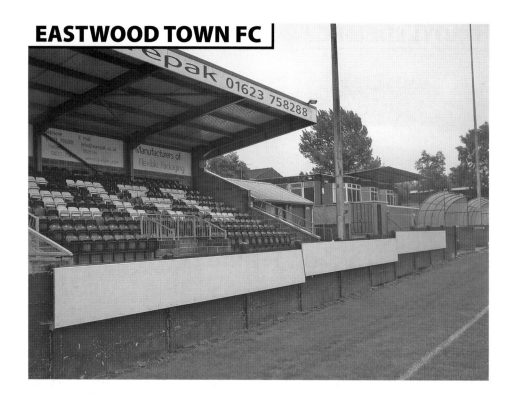

Founded: 1953
Former Names: None
Nickname: 'The Badgers'
Ground: Coronation Park, Chewton Street,
Eastwood   NG16 3HB
Record Attendance: 2,723 (February 1965)
Pitch Size: 115 × 77 yards

Colours: Black and White striped shirts, Black shorts
Clubhouse Telephone Nº: (01773) 715823
Office Telephone Nº: (01773) 711819
Fax Number: (01773) 711819
Ground Capacity: 3,146
Seating Capacity: 645
Web site: www.eastwoodtownfc.co.uk

GENERAL INFORMATION

Car Parking: At the ground
Coach Parking: At the ground
Nearest Railway Station: Langley Mill (1 mile)
Nearest Bus Station: Nottingham
Club Shop: At the ground
Opening Times: Matchdays only
Telephone Nº: (01773) 715823 or (01773) 711819

GROUND INFORMATION

Away Supporters' Entrances & Sections:
No usual segregation

ADMISSION INFO (2011/2012 PRICES)

Adult Standing/Seating: £10.00
Under-12s Standing/Seating: £3.00
Senior Citizen Standing/Seating: £7.00
Programme Price: £2.00

DISABLED INFORMATION

Wheelchairs: Accommodated
Helpers: Admitted
Prices: Normal prices apply
Disabled Toilets: Available
Contact: (01773) 715823   (Bookings are not necessary)

Travelling Supporters' Information:
Routes: From the North: Exit the M1 at Junction 27 and take the 3rd exit at the roundabout towards Heanor (A608). Follow the road past the Sandhills Tavern to a T-junction signposted for Brinsley/Heanor and continue along the A608. Follow the road through Brinsley into Eastwood then turn left at the lights into Nottingham Road. Look for the Fire Station on the right, then take the first right into Chewton Street. The Ground is on the right after 150 metres; From the South: Exit the M1 at Junction 26 and follow the A610 towards Ripley. Exit the A610 at the first junction signposted for Ilkeston and turn right onto the B6010, following the signs for Eastwood. Take the first left after the Man In Space pub into Chewton Street. The ground is on the right.

FC HALIFAX TOWN

Founded: 1911 (Re-formed 2008)
Former Names: Halifax Town FC
Nickname: 'The Shaymen'
Ground: The Shay Stadium, Shay Syke, Halifax, HX1 2YT
Ground Capacity: 10,568
Seating Capacity: 5,285

Record Attendance: 4,023 (1st January 2011)
Pitch Size: 112 × 73 yards
Colours: Blue shirts and shorts
Telephone Nº: (01422) 341222 (to change during
Fax Number: (01422) 349487 the 2011/12 season)
Web Site: www.halifaxafc.co.uk

GENERAL INFORMATION

Car Parking: Adjacent to the East Stand and also Shaw Hill Car Park (Nearby)
Coach Parking: By arrangement with the Club Secretary
Nearest Railway Station: Halifax (10 minutes walk)
Nearest Bus Station: Halifax (15 minutes walk)
Club Shop: At the ground in the East Stand
Opening Times: Please phone for details
Telephone Nº: (01422) 341222 (to change during the 2011/12 season)

GROUND INFORMATION

Away Supporters' Entrances & Sections:
Skircoat Stand (Seating only)

ADMISSION INFO (2011/2012 PRICES)

Adult Standing/Seating: £12.50
Under-16s Standing/Seating: £7.50
Senior Citizen Standing/Seating: £9.50
Under-12s Standing/Seating: £5.00
Under-7s Standing/Seating: £2.00
Programme Price: £3.00

DISABLED INFORMATION

Wheelchairs: 33 spaces available in total in disabled sections in the East Stand and South Stand
Helpers: One admitted free with each paying disabled fan
Prices: Free of charge for the disabled and helpers
Disabled Toilets: Available in the East and South Stands
Contact: (01422) 434212 (Bookings are not necessary)

Travelling Supporters' Information:
Routes: From the North: Take the A629 to Halifax Town Centre. Take the 2nd exit at the roundabout into Broad Street and follow signs for Huddersfield (A629) into Skircoat Road; From the South, East and West: Exit the M62 at Junction 24 and follow Halifax (A629) signs for the Town Centre into Skircoat Road then Shaw Hill for ground.

GAINSBOROUGH TRINITY FC

Founded: 1873
Former Names: None
Nickname: 'The Blues'
Ground: Northolme, Gainsborough, Lincolnshire, DN21 2QW
Record Attendance: 9,760 (1948)
Pitch Size: 111 × 71 yards

Colours: Blue shirts and shorts
Telephone Nº: (01427) 613295
Clubhouse Phone Nº: (01427) 613688
Fax Number: (01427) 613295
Ground Capacity: 4,340
Seating Capacity: 504
Web site: www.gainsboroughtrinity.com

GENERAL INFORMATION

Car Parking: Street parking and also in a Local Authority Car Park 150 yards from the ground towards the Town Centre
Coach Parking: Available by prior arrangement
Nearest Railway Station: Lea Road (2 miles)
Nearest Bus Station: Heaton Street (1 mile)
Club Shop: At the ground
Opening Times: Matchdays only
Telephone Nº: (01427) 611612

GROUND INFORMATION

Away Supporters' Entrances & Sections:
No usual segregation

ADMISSION INFO (2011/2012 PRICES)

Adult Standing: £10.00
Adult Seating: £11.00
Concessionary Standing: £6.00
Concessionary Seating: £7.00
Under-16s Standing/Seating: £2.00
Under-11s Standing/Seating: £1.00
Programme Price: £1.50

DISABLED INFORMATION

Wheelchairs: Accommodated
Helpers: Please phone the club for information
Prices: Normal prices for the disabled. Free for helpers
Disabled Toilets: Available in new block adjacent to the Main Stand
Contact: (01427) 613295 (Bookings are not necessary)

Travelling Supporters' Information:
Routes: From the North, South and West: Exit the A1 at Blyth services taking the 1st left through to Bawtry. In Bawtry, turn right at the traffic lights onto the A631 straight through to Gainsborough (approx. 11 miles). Go over the bridge to the second set of traffic lights and turn left onto the A159 (Scunthorpe Road). Follow the main road past Tesco on the right through the traffic lights. The ground is situated on right approximately a third of a mile north of the Town Centre; From the East: Take the A631 into Gainsborough and turn right onto the A159. Then as above.

GLOUCESTER CITY FC

Gloucester City are groundsharing with Cheltenham Town FC for the 2011/2012 season.

Founded: 1889 (**Re-formed**: 1980)
Former Names: Gloucester YMCA
Nickname: 'The Tigers'
Ground: Abbey Business Stadium, Whaddon Road, Cheltenham, Gloucestershire GL52 5NA
Ground Capacity: 7,136
Seating Capacity: 4,054

Record Attendance: 8,326 (1956)
Pitch Size: 110 × 72 yards
Colours: Yellow and Black Striped shirts, Black shorts
Telephone Nº: 07813 931781
Web Site: www.gloucestercityafc.com
E-mail: contact@gloucestercityafc.com

GENERAL INFORMATION

Car Parking: Very limited parking available at the ground. A Park & Ride scheme runs from Cheltenham Race Course and other car parks are available in Cheltenham Town Centre
Coach Parking: At the ground
Nearest Railway Station: Cheltenham Spa (2½ miles)
Nearest Bus Station: Cheltenham Royal Well
Club Shop: At the ground
Opening Times: Matchdays only

GROUND INFORMATION

Away Supporters' Entrances & Sections:
No usual segregation

ADMISSION INFO (2011/2012 PRICES)

Adult Standing: £12.00
Adult Seating: £12.00
Child Standing: £6.00
Child Seating: £6.00
Concessionary Standing: £6.00
Concessionary Seating: £6.00
Programme Price: £1.50

DISABLED INFORMATION

Wheelchairs: Accommodated in front of the Stagecoach West Stand (use main entrance) and in the In 2 Print Stand
Helpers: Admitted free of charge
Prices: Normal prices apply for disabled fans
Disabled Toilets: Available in the In 2 Print Stand, adjacent to the Stagecoach West Stand and in the Social Club
Contact: 07813 931781

Travelling Supporters' Information:
Routes: The ground is situated to the North-East of Cheltenham, 1 mile from the Town Centre off the B4632 (Prestbury Road) – Whaddon Road is to the East of the B4632 just North of Pittville Circus. Road signs in the vicinity indicate 'Whaddon Road/Cheltenham Town FC'.

GUISELEY AFC

Founded: 1909
Former Names: None
Nickname: 'The Lions'
Ground: Nethermoor, Otley Road, Guiseley, Leeds, LS20 8BT
Record Attendance: 2,486 (1989/90)
Pitch Size: 110 × 69 yards

Colours: White shirts with Navy Blue shorts
Telephone Nº: (01943) 873223
Social Club Phone Nº: (01943) 872872
Fax Number: (01943) 873223
Ground Capacity: 3,000
Seating Capacity: 500
Web site: www.guiseleyafc.co.uk

GENERAL INFORMATION

Car Parking: At the ground and in Ings Crescent
Coach Parking: At the ground
Nearest Railway Station: Guiseley (5 minute walk)
Nearest Bus Station: Bus Stop outside the ground
Club Shop: At the ground
Opening Times: Matchdays only
Telephone Nº: (01943) 879236 (weekdays)
Postal Sales: Yes

GROUND INFORMATION

Away Supporters' Entrances & Sections:
No usual segregation

ADMISSION INFO (2011/2012 PRICES)

Adult Standing: £10.00
Adult Seating: £9.00
Under-12s Standing: £1.00
Under-12s Seating: £1.00
Concessionary Standing: £6.00
Concessionary Seating: £6.00
Programme Price: £1.50

DISABLED INFORMATION

Wheelchairs: Accommodated by the Players' Entrance
Helpers: Admitted
Prices: Free for both disabled fans and helpers
Disabled Toilets: None
Contact: (01943) 879236 (Bookings are advisable)

Travelling Supporters' Information:
Routes: Exit the M62 at Junction 28 and take the Leeds Ring Road to the roundabout at the junction of the A65 at Horsforth. Turn left onto the A65 and pass through Rawdon to Guiseley keeping Morrison's supermarket on your left. Pass straight through the traffic lights with the Station pub or your right and the ground is on the right after ¼ mile, adjacent to the cricket field.

HARROGATE TOWN FC

Founded: 1919
Former Names: Harrogate FC and Harrogate Hotspurs FC
Nickname: 'Town'
Ground: CNG Stadium, Wetherby Road, Harrogate, HG2 7SA
Record Attendance: 4,280 (1950)

Pitch Size: 107 × 72 yards
Colours: Yellow and Black striped shirts, Black shorts
Telephone Nº: (01423) 880675 or 883671
Club Fax Number: (01423) 880675
Ground Capacity: 3,290
Seating Capacity: 502
Web site: www.harrogatetown.com

GENERAL INFORMATION

Car Parking: Hospital Car Park adjacent
Coach Parking: At the ground
Nearest Railway Station: Harrogate (¾ mile)
Nearest Bus Station: Harrogate
Club Shop: At the ground
Opening Times: Monday to Friday 9.00am to 3.00pm and also on Matchdays
Telephone Nº: (01423) 885525

GROUND INFORMATION

Away Supporters' Entrances & Sections:
No usual segregation

ADMISSION INFO (2011/2012 PRICES)

Adult Standing: £10.00
Adult Seating: £10.00
Concessionary Standing: £5.00
Concessionary Seating: £5.00
Under-16s Standing: £2.00 (when with a paying adult)
Under-16s Seating: £2.00 (when with a paying adult)
Programme Price: £2.00

DISABLED INFORMATION

Wheelchairs: Accommodated at the front of the Main Stand
Helpers: One helper admitted for each disabled fan
Prices: Free of charge for each disabled fan and helper
Disabled Toilets: Available
Contact: (01423) 880675 (Bookings are necessary)

Travelling Supporters' Information:
Routes: From the South: Take the A61 from Leeds and turn right at the roundabout onto the ring road (signposted York). After about 1¼ miles turn left at the next roundabout onto A661 Wetherby Road. The ground is situated ¾ mile on the right; From the West: Take the A59 straight into Wetherby Road from Empress Roundabout and the ground is on the left; From the East & North: Exit the A1(M) at Junction 47, take the A59 to Harrogate then follow the Southern bypass to Wetherby Road for the A661 Roundabout. Turn right towards Harrogate Town Centre and the ground is on the right after ¾ mile.

HINCKLEY UNITED FC

Founded: 1889

Former Names: Formed when Hinckley Athletic FC merged with Hinckley Town FC in 1997 (previously Westfield Rovers FC)

Nickname: 'The Knitters'

Ground: Greene King Stadium, Leicester Road, Hinckley   LE10 3DR

Record Attendance: 3,231 (1st July 2008)

Pitch Size: 110 × 72 yards

Colours: Shirts are Red with Blue trim, Blue shorts

Telephone N°: (01455) 840088

Contact Number: (01455) 840088

Ground Capacity: 4,329

Seating Capacity: 630

Web site: www.hinckleyunitedfc.co.uk

GENERAL INFORMATION

Car Parking: At the ground (£2.00 charge per car)

Coach Parking: At the ground

Nearest Railway Station: Hinckley (2 miles)

Nearest Bus Station: Hinckley

Club Shop: At the ground

Opening Times: Matchdays only

Telephone N°: (01455) 840088

GROUND INFORMATION

Away Supporters' Entrances & Sections:

West Stand and Terrace if required (no usual segregation)

ADMISSION INFO (2011/2012 PRICES)

Adult Standing: £10.00

Adult Seating: £12.00

Under-16s Standing: Free of charge

Under-16s Seating: £2.00

Senior Citizen Standing: £7.00

Senior Citizen Seating: £9.00

Programme Price: £2.00

DISABLED INFORMATION

Wheelchairs: Accommodated

Helpers: Admitted

Prices: Normal prices apply

Disabled Toilets: Yes

Contact: (01455) 840088   (Bookings are not necessary)

Travelling Supporters' Information:

Routes: From the North-West: Take the A5 southbound and take the 1st exit at Dodwells roundabout onto the A47 towards Earl Shilton. Go straight on over 3 roundabouts then take the 3rd exit at the next roundabout onto the B4668. The entrance to the ground is on the right after 200 yards; From the South: Take the A5 northbound and upon reaching Dodwells roundabout take the 2nd exit onto the A47 towards East Shilton. Then as above; From the North-East: Take the M69, exit at Junction 2 and follow the B4669 towards Hinckley. After 2 miles (passing through 2 sets of traffic lights) bear right into Spa Lane then turn right at the next set of traffic lights onto the B4668 towards Earl Shilton. The Stadium is on the left after 1¾ miles.

HISTON FC

Founded: 1904
Former Names: Histon Institute FC
Nickname: 'The Stutes'
Ground: The Glass World Stadium, Bridge Road, Impington, Cambridge CB24 9PH
Record Attendance: 6,400 (1956)
Pitch Size: 110 × 75 yards

Colours: Red and Black striped shirts, Black shorts
Telephone Nº: (01223) 237373
Fax Number: (01223) 237495
Ground Capacity: 4,100
Seating Capacity: 1,626
Web site: www.histonfc.co.uk

GENERAL INFORMATION

Car Parking: Permit holders and disabled parking only at the ground. Check web site for details of fans parking
Coach Parking: For team coaches only
Nearest Railway Station: Cambridge (4 miles)
Nearest Bus Station: Cambridge (4 miles) (Use Citi Seven service for the ground)
Club Shop: At the ground
Opening Times: Three hours prior to kick-off for both Saturday and evening matches.
Telephone Nº: (01223) 237373

GROUND INFORMATION

Away Supporters' Entrances & Sections:
No usual segregation

ADMISSION INFO (2011/2012 PRICES)

Adult Standing: £10.00
Adult Seating: £10.00
Child Standing: £3.00
Child Seating: £3.00
Senior Citizen Standing: £6.00
Senior Citizen Seating: £6.00
Programme Price: £2.50

DISABLED INFORMATION

Wheelchairs: 6 spaces available in the home section and 6 spaces available in the away section
Helpers: Admitted
Prices: Normal prices apply for the disabled. Free for helpers
Disabled Toilets: Available in both the home and away sections
Contact: Mac McDonald (Club safety officer) 07730 557021

Travelling Supporters' Information:
Routes: Exit the M11 at Junction 14 and follow the A14 eastwards. Take the first exit onto the B1049 (signposted Histon & Cottenham). Turn left at the traffic lights at the top of the slip road and pass the Holiday Inn on the right. Continue over the bridge and the entrance to the ground is on the right.

HYDE FC

Founded: 1919
Former Names: Hyde FC (1885-1917) and Hyde United FC (1917-2010)
Nickname: 'Tigers'
Ground: Tameside Stadium, Ewen Fields, Walker Lane, Hyde, Cheshire SK14 5PL
Record Attendance: 9,500 (1952)
Pitch Size: 114 × 70 yards

Colours: White shirts with Navy Blue shorts
Telephone Nº: 0871 200-2116 (Matchdays) or 07778 792502 (Secretary)
Fax Number: 0871 200-2118 (Ground); (01270) 212473 (Secretary)
Ground Capacity: 4,250
Seating Capacity: 550
Web site: www.hydefc.co.uk

GENERAL INFORMATION

Car Parking: 150 spaces available at the ground
Coach Parking: At the ground
Nearest Railway Station: Newton (¼ mile)
Nearest Bus Station: Hyde
Club Shop: At the ground
Opening Times: Matchdays only
Telephone Nº: 0871 200-2116

GROUND INFORMATION

Away Supporters' Entrances & Sections:
No usual segregation although it is used as required

ADMISSION INFO (2011/2012 PRICES)

Adult Standing: £10.00
Adult Seating: £12.00
Child Standing: £4.00
Child Seating: £6.00
Senior Citizen Standing: £4.00
Senior Citizen Seating: £6.00
Programme Price: £2.00

DISABLED INFORMATION

Wheelchairs: Accommodated in the disabled area
Helpers: Please phone the club for information
Prices: Please phone the club for information
Disabled Toilets: Yes
Contact: (01270) 212473 (Bookings are not necessary)

Travelling Supporters' Information:
Routes: Exit the M60 at Junction 24 and then exit the M67 at Junction 3 for Hyde. Turn right at the top of the slip road, left at the lights (Morrisons on the left). Turn right at the next set of lights into Lumn Road then turn left at the Give Way sign into Walker Lane. Take the 2nd Car Park entrance near the Leisure Pool and follow the road round for the Stadium.

NUNEATON TOWN FC

Founded: 1937 (Reformed 2008)
Former Names: Nuneaton Borough FC
Nickname: 'Boro'
Ground: Triton Showers Community Arena,
Liberty Way, Attleborough Fields Industrial Estate,
Nuneaton   CV11 6RR
Record Attendance: 3,111 (2nd May 2009)
Pitch Size: 109 × 74 yards

Colours: Blue shirts and white shorts
Telephone No: (024) 7638-5738
Daytime Phone No: (024) 7638-5738
Fax Number: (024) 7637-2995
Ground Capacity: 4,500
Seating Capacity: 500
Web site: www.nuneatontownfc.com

GENERAL INFORMATION

Car Parking: On-site car park plus various other parking
spaces available on the nearby Industrial Estate
Coach Parking: At the ground
Nearest Railway Station: Nuneaton (2 miles)
Nearest Bus Station: Nuneaton (2 miles)
Club Shop: Yes – The Boro Shop
Opening Times: By appointment and also on matchdays
Telephone No: (024) 7638-5738

GROUND INFORMATION

Away Supporters' Entrances & Sections:
No usual segregation

ADMISSION INFO (2011/2012 PRICES)

Adult Standing: £12.00
Adult Seating: £14.00
Concessionary Standing: £8.00
Concessionary Seating: £10.00
Under-16s Standing/Seating: £5.00
Under-12s Standing/Seating: £2.00
Under-5s Standing/Seating: Free of charge
Programme Price: £2.50

DISABLED INFORMATION

Wheelchairs: Accommodated
Helpers: Please phone the club for information
Prices: Please phone the club for information
Disabled Toilets: Available
Contact: (024) 7638-5738   (Bookings are necessary)

Travelling Supporters' Information:
Routes: From the South, West and North-West: Exit the M6 at Junction 3 and follow the A444 into Nuneaton. At the Coton
Arches roundabout turn right into Avenue Road which is the A4254 signposted for Hinckley. Continue along the A4254 following
the road into Garrett Street then Eastboro Way then turn left into Townsend Drive. Follow the road round before turning left into
Liberty Way for the ground; From the North: Exit the M1 at Junction 21 and follow the M69. Exit the M69 at Junction 1 and
take the 4th exit at the roundabout onto the A5 (Tamworth, Nuneaton). At Longshoot Junction, turn left onto the A47, continue
to the roundabout and take the 1st exit onto A4254 Eastborough Way. Turn right at the next roundabout into Townsend Drive
then immediately right again for Liberty Way.

SOLIHULL MOORS FC

Founded: 2007
Former Names: Formed by the merger of Solihull Borough FC and Moor Green FC in 2007
Nickname: 'The Moors'
Ground: Damson Park, Damson Parkway, Solihull, B91 2PP
Record Attendance: 2,000 (vs Birmingham City)

Pitch Size: 110 × 75 yards
Colours: White shirts with Black shorts
Telephone Nº: (0121) 705-6770
Fax Number: (0121) 711-4045
Ground Capacity: 3,050
Seating Capacity: 280
Web site: www.solihullmoorsfc.co.uk

GENERAL INFORMATION

Car Parking: At the ground
Coach Parking: At the ground
Nearest Railway Station: Birmingham International (2 miles)
Nearest Bus Station: Birmingham (5 miles)
Club Shop: At the ground
Opening Times: Matchdays only
Telephone Nº: (0121) 705-6770

GROUND INFORMATION

Away Supporters' Entrances & Sections:
No usual segregation

ADMISSION INFO (2011/2012 PRICES)

Adult Standing: £10.00
Adult Seating: £10.00
Senior Citizen/Junior Standing: £5.00
Senior Citizen/Junior Seating: £5.00
Note: Under-16s can purchase a season ticket for £30.00
Programme Price: £2.00

DISABLED INFORMATION

Wheelchairs: Spaces for 3 wheelchairs are available
Helpers: Admitted
Prices: Normal prices apply
Disabled Toilets: Available
Contact: (0121) 705-6770

Travelling Supporters' Information:
Routes: Exit the M42 at Junction 6 and take the A45 for 2 miles towards Birmingham. Turn left at the traffic lights near the Posthouse Hotel into Damson Parkway (signposted for Landrover/Damsonwood). Continue to the roundabout and come back along the other carriageway to the ground which is situated on the left after about 150 yards.

STALYBRIDGE CELTIC FC

Founded: 1909
Former Names: None
Nickname: 'Celtic'
Ground: Bower Fold, Mottram Road, Stalybridge, Cheshire SK15 2RT
Record Attendance: 9,753 (1922/23)
Pitch Size: 109 × 70 yards

Colours: Blue shirts, White shorts and Blue socks
Telephone Nº: (0161) 338-2828
Daytime Phone Nº: (0161) 338-2828
Fax Number: (0161) 338-8256
Ground Capacity: 6,108
Seating Capacity: 1,155
Web site: www.stalybridgeceltic.co.uk

GENERAL INFORMATION

Car Parking: At the ground (£1.00 charge)
Coach Parking: At the ground
Nearest Railway Station: Stalybridge (1 mile)
Nearest Bus Station: Stalybridge town centre
Club Shop: At the ground and also at "Stitch in Time", Market Street, Stalybridge
Opening Times: Matchdays only at the ground
Monday to Friday 9.00am to 5.00pm at Market Street
Telephone Nº: (0161) 338-2828

GROUND INFORMATION

Away Supporters' Entrances & Sections:
Lockwood & Greenwood Stand on the few occasions when segregation is required. No usual segregation

ADMISSION INFO (2011/2012 PRICES)

Adult Standing: £10.00
Adult Seating: £10.00
Concessionary Standing: £6.00
Concessionary Seating: £6.00
Note: Under-12s are admitted for £1.00 when accompanied by a paying adult
Programme Price: £2.00

DISABLED INFORMATION

Wheelchairs: 20 spaces available each for home and away fans at the side of the Stepan Stand. A further 9 spaces available in the new Lord Tom Pendry Stand
Helpers: Please phone the club for information
Prices: Please phone the club for information
Disabled Toilets: Available at the rear of the Stepan Stand and at the side of the Lord Tom Pendry Stand
Contact: (0161) 338-2828   (Bookings are necessary)

Travelling Supporters' Information:
Routes: From the Midlands and South: Take the M6, M56, M60 and M67, leaving at the end of the motorway. Go across the roundabout to the traffic lights and turn left. The ground is approximately 2 miles on the left before the Hare & Hounds pub; From the North: Exit the M62 at Junction 18 onto the M60 singposted for Ashton-under-Lyne. Follow the M60 to Junction 24 and join the M67, then as from the Midlands and South.

VAUXHALL MOTORS FC

Founded: 1963
Former Names: Vauxhall GM FC
Nickname: 'Motormen'
Ground: Rivacre Park, Rivacre Road, Hooton, Ellesmere Port, Cheshire   CH66 1NJ
Record Attendance: 1,500 (1987)
Pitch Size: 117 × 78 yards
Colours: White shirts with Blue shorts

Telephone Nº: (0151) 328-1114 (Ground)
Ground Capacity: 3,306
Seating Capacity: 266
Contact: Mike Harper
Contact Phone Nº: (0151) 645-4561
Contact Mobile Nº: 07817 400202
Web site: www.vmfc.com
E-mail: office@vmfc.com

GENERAL INFORMATION

Car Parking: At the ground
Coach Parking: At the ground
Nearest Railway Station: Overpool
Nearest Bus Station: Ellesmere Port
Club Shop: At the ground
Opening Times: Matchdays only
Telephone Nº: None

GROUND INFORMATION

Away Supporters' Entrances & Sections:
No usual segregation

ADMISSION INFO (2011/2012 PRICES)

Adult Standing: £9.00
Adult Seating: £9.00
Child Standing: £1.00
Child Seating: £1.00
Senior Citizen Standing/Seating: £6.00
Student Standing/Seating: £3.00
Programme Price: £2.00

DISABLED INFORMATION

Wheelchairs: Accommodated as necessary
Helpers: Admitted
Prices: Normal prices for the disabled. Free for carers
Disabled Toilets: Available
Contact: – (Bookings are not necessary)

Travelling Supporters' Information:
Routes: Exit the M53 at Junction 5 and take the A41 towards Chester. Turn left at the first set of traffic lights into Hooton Green. Turn left at the first T-junction then right at the next T-junction into Rivacre Road. The ground is situated 250 yards on the right.

WORCESTER CITY FC

Founded: 1902
Former Names: Berwick Rangers FC
Nickname: 'The City'
Ground: St. George's Lane, Worcester WR1 1QT
Record Attendance: 17,042 (1958/59)
Pitch Size: 110 × 75 yards

Colours: Blue and White shirts with Blue shorts
Telephone Nº: (01905) 23003
Fax Number: (01905) 26668
Ground Capacity: 4,500
Seating Capacity: 1,100
Web site: www.worcestercityfc.co.uk

GENERAL INFORMATION

Car Parking: Street parking
Coach Parking: Street parking
Nearest Railway Station: Foregate Street (1 mile)
Nearest Bus Station: Crowngate Bus Station
Club Shop: At the ground
Opening Times: Monday to Friday and Matchdays from 10.00am to 5.00pm
Telephone Nº: (01905) 23003

GROUND INFORMATION

Away Supporters' Entrances & Sections:
Turnstile at the Canal End when segregation is in force for Canal End accommodation

ADMISSION INFO (2011/2012 PRICES)

Adult Standing: £11.00
Adult Seating: £13.00
Under-16s Standing: £3.00
Under-16s Seating: £5.00
Senior Citizen Standing: £7.00
Senior Citizen Seating: £9.00
Programme Price: £2.50

DISABLED INFORMATION

Wheelchairs: 3 covered spaces available
Helpers: Admitted
Prices: Normal prices apply for the disabled. Helpers are admitted free of charge
Disabled Toilets: None
Contact: (01905) 23003 (Bookings are necessary)

Travelling Supporters' Information:
Routes: Exit the M5 at Junction 6 and take the A449 Kidderminster Road. Follow to the end of the dual carriageway and take the second exit at the roundabout for Worcester City Centre. At the first set of traffic lights turn right into the town centre. The 3rd turning on the left is St. George's Lane North.

WORKINGTON AFC

Founded: 1884 (Reformed 1921)
Former Names: None
Nickname: 'Reds'
Ground: Borough Park, Workington   CA14 2DT
Record Attendance: 21,000 (vs Manchester United)
Pitch Size: 112 × 72 yards

Colours: Red shirts and shorts
Telephone Nº: (01900) 602871
Fax Number: (01900) 67432
Ground Capacity: 3,100
Seating Capacity: 500
Web site: www.workingtonafc.com

GENERAL INFORMATION

Car Parking: Car Park next to the ground
Coach Parking: At the ground
Nearest Railway Station: Workington (¼ mile)
Nearest Bus Station: Workington (½ mile)
Club Shop: At the ground
Opening Times: Matchdays only
Telephone Nº: (01946) 832710

GROUND INFORMATION

Away Supporters' Entrances & Sections:
No usual segregation

ADMISSION INFO (2011/2012 PRICES)

Adult Standing: £12.00
Adult Seating: £12.00
Senior Citizen/Junior/Student Standing: £7.00
Senior Citizen/Junior/Student Seating: £7.00
Note: Under-5s are admitted free of charge
Programme Price: £2.00

DISABLED INFORMATION

Wheelchairs: Accommodated
Helpers: Admitted
Prices: Normal prices apply
Disabled Toilets: Available
Contact: (01900) 602871   (Bookings are not necessary)

Travelling Supporters' Information:
Routes: Exit the M6 at Junction 40 and take the A66 towards Keswick and Workington. Upon reaching Workington, continue until you reach the traffic lights at the bottom of the hill (with HSBC Bank facing) and turn left towards the town centre. Approach the traffic lights in the middle lane with the Washington Central Hotel on the right and turn right. Continue along this road, crossing a mini-roundabout, a pedestrian crossing and a further set of traffic lights. Upon reaching the railway station, pass through the junction and bear right passing the Derwent Park Rugby League Stadium then bear left and Borough Park is straight ahead.

THE FOOTBALL CONFERENCE
BLUE SQUARE SOUTH

Address

Third Floor, Wellington House,
31-34 Waterloo Street, Birmingham   B2 5TJ

Phone (0121) 214-1950

Web site   www.footballconference.co.uk

Clubs for the 2011/2012 Season

BASINGSTOKE TOWN FC

Founded: 1896	**Colours**: Yellow and Blue shirts with Blue shorts
Former Names: None	**Telephone N°**: (01256) 327575
Nickname: 'Dragons'	**Fax Number**: (01256) 326346
Ground: The Camrose Ground, Western Way,	**Social Club N°**: (01256) 464353
Basingstoke, Hants. RG22 6EZ	**Ground Capacity**: 6,000
Record Attendance: 5,085 (25th November 1997)	**Seating Capacity**: 650
Pitch Size: 110 × 70 yards	**Web site**: www.basingstoketown.net

GENERAL INFORMATION

Car Parking: 600 spaces available at the ground
Coach Parking: Ample room available at ground
Nearest Railway Station: Basingstoke
Nearest Bus Station: Basingstoke Town Centre (2 miles)
Club Shop: The Camrose Shop
Opening Times: Matchdays only
Telephone N°: (01256) 327575

GROUND INFORMATION

Away Supporters' Entrances & Sections:
No usual segregation

ADMISSION INFO (2011/2012 PRICES)

Adult Standing: £12.00
Adult Seating: £13.00
Concessionary Standing: £7.00
Concessionary Seating: £8.00
Under-16s Standing: £3.00
Under-16s Seating: £4.00
Programme Price: £2.50

DISABLED INFORMATION

Wheelchairs: 6 spaces are available under cover
Helpers: Admitted
Prices: Normal prices for the disabled. Free for helpers
Disabled Toilets: Yes
Contact: (01256) 327575 (Bookings are not necessary)

Travelling Supporters' Information:
Routes: Exit the M3 at Junction 6 and take the 1st left at the Black Dam roundabout. At the next roundabout take the 2nd exit, then the 1st exit at the following roundabout and the 5th exit at the next roundabout. This takes you into Western Way and the ground is 50 yards on the right.

BOREHAM WOOD FC

Founded: 1948
Former Names: Boreham Rovers FC and Royal Retournez FC
Nickname: 'The Wood'
Ground: Meadow Park, Broughinge Road, Boreham Wood, Hertfordshire WD6 5AL
Record Attendance: 4,030 (2002)
Pitch Size: 112 × 72 yards

Colours: White shirts with Black shorts
Telephone Nº: (0208) 953-5097
Fax Number: (0208) 207-7982
Ground Capacity: 4,239
Seating Capacity: 500
Web site: www.borehamwoodfootballclub.co.uk

GENERAL INFORMATION

Car Parking: At the ground
Coach Parking: At the ground
Nearest Railway Station: Elstree & Boreham Wood (1 mile)
Nearest Bus Station: Barnet
Club Shop: At the ground
Opening Times: 11.00am to 10.00pm Monday to Thursday; 11.00am to 6.00pm at weekends
Telephone Nº: (0208) 953-5097

GROUND INFORMATION

Away Supporters' Entrances & Sections:
No usual segregation

ADMISSION INFO (2011/2012 PRICES)

Adult Standing: £11.00
Adult Seating: £11.00
Child Standing: £6.00
Child Seating: £6.00
Programme Price: £2.00

DISABLED INFORMATION

Wheelchairs: Accommodated
Helpers: Admitted
Prices: Concessionary prices are charged for the disabled and helpers
Disabled Toilets: None
Contact: (0208) 953-5097   (Bookings are necessary)

Travelling Supporters' Information:
Routes: Exit the M25 at Junction 23 and take the A1 South. After 2 miles, take the Boreham Wood exit onto the dual carriageway and go over the flyover following signs for Boreham Wood for 1 mile. Turn right at the Studio roundabout into Brook Road, then next right into Broughinge Road for the ground.

BROMLEY FC

Founded: 1892
Former Names: None
Nickname: 'Lillywhites'
Ground: The Stadium, Hayes Lane, Bromley, Kent, BR2 9EF
Record Attendance: 12,000 (24th September 1949)
Pitch Size: 112 × 72 yards

Colours: White shirts with Black shorts
Telephone Nº: (020) 8460-5291
Fax Number: –
Ground Capacity: 3,300
Seating Capacity: 1,300
Web site: www.bromleyfc.net

GENERAL INFORMATION

Car Parking: 300 spaces available at the ground
Coach Parking: At the ground
Nearest Railway Station: Bromley South (1 mile)
Nearest Bus Station: High Street, Bromley
Club Shop: At the ground
Opening Times: Matchdays only
Telephone Nº: (020) 8460-5291

GROUND INFORMATION

Away Supporters' Entrances & Sections:
No usual segregation

ADMISSION INFO (2011/2012 PRICES)

Adult Standing/Seating: £12.00
Concessionary Standing/Seating: £6.00
Under-16s/Student Standing/Seating: £5.00
Note: Under-5s are admitted free of charge
Programme Price: £2.00

DISABLED INFORMATION

Wheelchairs: Accommodated
Helpers: Admitted
Prices: Please phone the club for information
Disabled Toilets: Yes
Contact: (0181) 460-5291 (Bookings are necessary)

Travelling Supporters' Information:
Routes: Exit the M25 at Junction 4 and follow the A21 for Bromley and London for approximately 4 miles before forking left onto the A232 signposted for Croydon/Sutton. At the second set of traffic lights turn right into Baston Road (B265) and follow for approximately 2 miles as it becomes Hayes Street and then Hayes Lane. The ground is on the right just after a mini-roundabout.

CHELMSFORD CITY FC

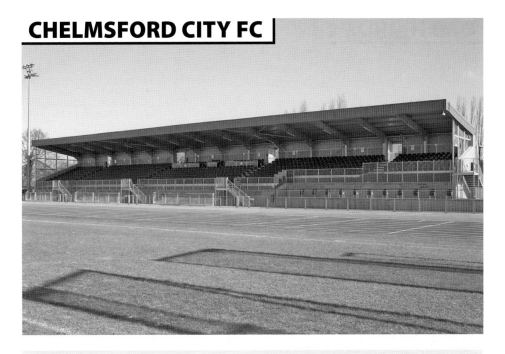

Founded: 1938
Former Names: Chelmsford FC
Nickname: 'City' or 'Clarets'
Ground: Melbourne Park, Salerno Way, Chelmsford, CM1 2EH
Record Attendance: 16,807 (at previous ground)
Pitch Size: 109 × 70 yards

Colours: Claret and White shirts and shorts
Telephone Nº: (01245) 290959
Fax Number: –
Ground Capacity: 3,000
Seating Capacity: 1,400
Web site: www.chelmsfordcityfc.com

GENERAL INFORMATION

Car Parking: Limited space at ground and street parking
Coach Parking: Two spaces available at the ground subject to advance notice
Nearest Railway Station: Chelmsford (2 miles)
Nearest Bus Station: Chelmsford (2 miles)
Club Shop: At the ground
Opening Times: Matchdays only at present
Telephone Nº: (01245) 290959

GROUND INFORMATION

Away Supporters' Entrances & Sections:
No usual segregation

ADMISSION INFO (2011/2012 PRICES)

Adult Standing: £11.50
Adult Seating: £12.50
Under-16s Standing: £3.50
Under-16s Seating: £4.50
Under-12s Standing: Free of charge
Under-12s Seating: £1.00
Concessionary Standing: £7.50
Concessionary Seating: £8.50
Programme Price: £2.50

DISABLED INFORMATION

Wheelchairs: Spaces for 11 wheelchairs available
Helpers: Admitted free of charge
Prices: Disabled fans are charged standing admission prices
Disabled Toilets: Available
Contact: (01245) 290959 (Bookings are necessary)

Travelling Supporters' Information:
Route: The ground is situated next to the only set of high rise flats in Chelmsford which can therefore be used as a landmark. From the A12 from London: Exit the A12 at Junction 15 signposted for Chelmsford/Harlow/A414 and head towards Chelmsford along the dual-carriageway. At the third roundabout, immediately after passing the 'Superbowl' on the left, take the first exit into Westway, signposted for the Crematorium and Widford Industrial Estate. Continue along Westway which becomes Waterhouse Lane after the second set of traffic lights. At the next set of lights (at the gyratory system) take the first exit into Rainsford Road, signposted for Sawbridgeworth A1060. Continue along Rainsford Road then turn right into Chignal Road at the second set of traffic lights. Turn right again into Melbourne Avenue and Salerno Way is on the left at the end of the football pitches.

DARTFORD FC

Founded: 1888
Former Names: None
Nickname: 'The Darts'
Ground: Princes Park Stadium, Grassbanks, Darenth Road, Dartford DA1 1RT
Record Attendance: 4,097 (11th November 2006)
Pitch Size: 110 × 71 yards

Colours: White Shirts with Black Shorts
Telephone Nº: (01322) 299990
Fax Number: (01322) 299996
Ground Capacity: 4,097
Seating Capacity: 640
Web Site: www.dartfordfc.co.uk

GENERAL INFORMATION

Car Parking: At the ground
Coach Parking: At the ground
Nearest Railway Station: Dartford (½ mile)
Nearest Bus Station: Dartford (½ mile) & Bluewater (2 miles)
Club Shop: At the ground
Opening Times: Matchdays only – 1.00pm to 6.00pm.
Telephone Nº: (01322) 299990

ADMISSION INFO (2011/2012 PRICES)

Adult Standing: £12.00
Adult Seating: £12.00
Senior Citizen/Concessionary Standing: £6.00
Senior Citizen/Concessionary Seating: £6.00
Under-12s Standing/Seating: £2.00
Programme Price: £2.00

DISABLED INFORMATION

Wheelchairs: Accommodated
Helpers: Admitted
Prices: Concessionary prices for the disabled and helpers
Disabled Toilets: Available
Contact: (01322) 299991 (Bookings are not necessary)

Travelling Supporters' Information:
Routes: From M25 Clockwise: Exit the M25 at Junction 1B. At the roundabout, take the 3rd exit onto Princes Road (A225) then the second exit at the next roundabout.* Continue downhill to the traffic lights (with the ground on the left), turn left into Darenth Road then take the 2nd left for the Car Park; From M25 Anti-clockwise: Exit the M25 at Junction 2 and follow the A225 to the roundabout. Take the first exit at this roundabout then the 2nd exit at the next roundabout. Then as from * above.

DORCHESTER TOWN FC

Founded: 1880
Former Names: None
Nickname: 'The Magpies'
Ground: The Avenue Stadium, Weymouth Avenue, Dorchester, Dorset   DT1 2RY
Record Attendance: 4,159 (1st January 1999)
Pitch Size: 110 × 80 yards

Colours: White shirts with Black shorts and socks
Telephone Nº: (01305) 262451
Fax Number: (01305) 267623
Ground Capacity: 5,009
Seating Capacity: 710
Web Site: www.dorchestertownfc.co.uk

GENERAL INFORMATION

Car Parking: 350 spaces available at the ground (£1.00 fee)
Coach Parking: At the ground
Nearest Railway Station: Dorchester South and West (both 1 mile)
Nearest Bus Station: Nearby
Club Shop: At the ground
Opening Times: During 1st team matchdays only
Telephone Nº: (01305) 262451

GROUND INFORMATION

Away Supporters' Entrances & Sections:
Main Stand side when segregated (not usual)

ADMISSION INFO (2011/2012 PRICES)

Adult Standing: £9.00
Adult Seating: £10.00
Senior Citizen/Child Standing: £5.50
Senior Citizen/Child Seating: £6.50
Under-16s: £2.50 when accompanied by a paying adult
Programme Price: £2.00

DISABLED INFORMATION

Wheelchairs: 10 spaces available each for home and away fans at the North West End of the terracing
Helpers: Admitted
Prices: Normal prices apply
Disabled Toilets: 2 available near the disabled area
Contact: (01305) 262451   (Bookings are not necessary)

Travelling Supporters' Information:
Routes: Take the Dorchester Bypass (A35) from all directions. The ground is on the South side of town, adjacent to a roundabout at the intersection with the A354 to Weymouth. Alternatively, take Weymouth signs from Dorchester Town Centre for 1½ miles.

DOVER ATHLETIC FC

Founded: 1983
Former Names: None
Nickname: 'The Whites'
Ground: Crabble Athletic Ground, Lewisham Road, River, Dover CT17 0JB
Record Attendance: 4,186 (2002)
Pitch Size: 111 × 73 yards

Colours: White shirts with Black shorts
Telephone Nº: (01304) 822373
Fax Number: (01304) 821383
Ground Capacity: 6,500
Seating Capacity: 1,000
Web site: www.dover-athletic.co.uk

GENERAL INFORMATION
Car Parking: Street parking
Coach Parking: Street parking
Nearest Railway Station: Kearsney (1 mile)
Nearest Bus Station: Pencester Road, Dover (1½ miles)
Club Shop: At the ground
Opening Times: Saturdays 9.00am to 12.00pm
Telephone Nº: (01304) 822373

GROUND INFORMATION
Away Supporters' Entrances & Sections:
Segregation only used when required

ADMISSION INFO (2011/2012 PRICES)
Adult Standing: £12.00
Adult Seating: £13.50
Senior Citizen Standing: £9.00
Senior Citizen Seating: £10.00
Under-18s Standing: £6.00 (Under-11s £3.00)
Under-18s Seating: £7.50 (Under-11s £3.00)
Programme Price: £2.00

DISABLED INFORMATION
Wheelchairs: Approximately 20 spaces are available in front of the Family Stand
Helpers: Please phone the club for information
Prices: Please phone the club for information
Disabled Toilets: None
Contact: – (Bookings are not necessary)

Travelling Supporters' Information:
Routes: Take the A2 to the Whitfield roundabout and take the 4th exit. Travel down the hill to the mini-roundabout then turn left and follow the road for 1 mile to the traffic lights on the hill. Turn sharp right and pass under the railway bridge – the ground is on the left after 300 yards.

EASTBOURNE BOROUGH FC

Founded: 1963
Former Names: Langney Sports FC
Nickname: 'The Sports'
Ground: Langney Sports Club, Priory Lane,
Eastbourne BN23 7QH
Record Attendance: 3,770 (5th November 2005)
Pitch Size: 115 × 72 yards

Colours: Red shirts with Black shorts
Telephone Nº: (01323) 766265
Fax Number: (01323) 741627
Ground Capacity: 4,400
Seating Capacity: 542
Web site: www.ebfc.co.uk

GENERAL INFORMATION

Car Parking: Around 400 spaces available at the ground
Coach Parking: At the ground
Nearest Railway Station: Pevensey & Westham (1½ miles but no public transport to the ground)
Nearest Bus Station: Eastbourne (Service 6A to ground)
Club Shop: At the ground
Opening Times: Matchdays only
Telephone Nº: (01323) 766265

GROUND INFORMATION

Away Supporters' Entrances & Sections:
No usual segregation

ADMISSION INFO (2011/2012 PRICES)

Adult Standing: £12.00
Adult Seating: £12.00
Under-16s Standing/Seating: £1.00
Senior Citizen Standing: £8.00
Senior Citizen Seating: £8.00
Programme Price: £2.50

DISABLED INFORMATION

Wheelchairs: 6 spaces available
Helpers: Admitted
Prices: Normal prices apply
Disabled Toilets: Available
Contact: (01323) 766265 (Bookings are necessary)

Travelling Supporters' Information:
Routes: From the North: Exit the A22 onto the Polegate bypass, signposted A27 Eastbourne, Hastings & Bexhill. *Take the 2nd exit at the next roundabout for Stone Cross and Westham (A22) then the first exit at the following roundabout signposted Stone Cross and Westham. Turn right after ½ mile into Friday Street (B2104). At the end of Friday Street, turn left at the double mini-roundabout into Hide Hollow (B2191), passing Eastbourne Crematorium on your right. Turn right at the roundabout into Priory Road, and Priory Lane is about 200 yards down the road on the left; Approaching on the A27 from Brighton: Turn left at the Polegate traffic lights then take 2nd exit at the large roundabout to join the bypass. Then as from *.

EASTLEIGH FC

Founded: 1946
Former Names: Swaythling Athletic FC and Swaythling FC
Nickname: 'The Spitfires'
Ground: Silverlake Stadium, Ten Acres, Stoneham Lane, Eastleigh   SO50 9HT
Record Attendance: 3,104 (2006)
Pitch Size: 112 × 74 yards

Colours: White shirts with Royal Blue shorts
Telephone N°: (023) 8061-3361
Fax Number: (023) 8061-2379
Ground Capacity: 3,000
Seating Capacity: 512
Web site: www.eastleigh-fc.co.uk
e-mail: commercial@eastleigh-fc.co.uk

GENERAL INFORMATION

Car Parking: Spaces for 450 cars available (hard standing)
Coach Parking: At the ground
Nearest Railway Station: Southampton Parkway (¾ mile)
Nearest Bus Station: Eastleigh (2 miles)
Club Shop: At the ground
Opening Times: Matchdays and during functions only

GROUND INFORMATION

Away Supporters' Entrances & Sections:
No usual segregation

ADMISSION INFO (2011/2012 PRICES)

Adult Standing/Seating: £12.00
Concessionary Standing/Seating: £7.50
Under-16s Standing/Seating: £4.00
Under-12s Standing/Seating: Free of charge
Programme Price: £2.00

DISABLED INFORMATION

Wheelchairs: Accommodated
Helpers: Admitted
Prices: Normal prices apply
Disabled Toilets: Available
Contact: (023) 8061-3361   (Bookings are not necessary)

Travelling Supporters' Information:
Routes: Exit the M27 at Junction 5 (signposted for Southampton Airport) and take the A335 (Stoneham Way) towards Southampton. After ½ mile, turn right at the traffic lights into Bassett Green Road. Turn right at the next set of traffic lights into Stoneham Lane and the ground is on the right after ¾ mile.

FARNBOROUGH FC

Founded: 1967   (Re-formed in 2007)
Former Names: Farnborough Town FC
Nickname: 'The Boro'
Ground: The Rushmoor Stadium, Cherrywood Road, Farnborough   GU14 8UD
Record Attendance: 4,267 (15th May 2011)
Pitch Size: 115 × 77 yards

Colours: Yellow and Blue shirts and shorts
Telephone Nº: 0844 807-9900
Fax Number: (01252) 372640
Ground Capacity: 5,600 at present
Seating Capacity: 3,135
Web site: www.farnboroughfc.co.uk
E-mail contact: admin@farnboroughfc.co.uk

GENERAL INFORMATION

Car Parking: 260 spaces available at the ground with a further 200 spaces at the nearby Sixth Form college
Coach Parking: At the ground
Nearest Railway Stations: Farnborough (Main), Farnborough North, Frimley and Blackwater
Nearest Bus Station: Buses from Farnborough Main stop just outside the ground – please check the web site for details.
Club Shop: At the ground + web sales in the near future
Opening Times: Matchdays only
Telephone Nº: 0844 807-8800

GROUND INFORMATION

Away Supporters' Entrances & Sections:
Moor Road entrances and accommodation

ADMISSION INFO (2011/2012 PRICES)

Adult Standing: £12.00
Adult Seating: £12.00
Concessionary Standing: £8.00
Concessionary Seating: £8.00
Under-16s Seating/Standing: £3.00
Note: In keeping with F.A. Regulations, the Club reserves the right to charge higher prices for F.A. Trophy and F.A. Cup games.
Programme Price: £2.50

DISABLED INFORMATION

Wheelchairs: Spaces available in a disabled section in the PRE Stand
Helpers: Admitted free of charge
Prices: Concessionary prices charged for disabled fans
Disabled Toilets: Available in the PRE Stand
Contact: 0844 807-9900   (Bookings are not necessary)

Travelling Supporters' Information:
Routes: Exit the M3 at Junction 4 and take the A331 signposted for Farnham. After a few hundred yards exit at the second slip road – signposted A325 Farnborough – turn right at the roundabout and cross over the dual carriageway and a small roundabout. Pass the Farnborough Gate shopping centre on your left and at the next roundabout turn left onto the A325. Go over a pelican crossing and at the next set of lights take the right filter lane into Prospect Avenue. At the end of this road turn right at the roundabout into Cherrywood Road. The ground is on the right after ½ mile.

HAMPTON & RICHMOND BOROUGH FC

Founded: 1921
Former Names: Hampton FC
Nickname: 'Beavers'
Ground: Beveree Stadium, Beaver Close, off Station Road, Hampton, Middlesex TW12 2BT
Record Attendance: 3,500 vs West Ham United
Pitch Size: 113 × 71 yards

Colours: Blue shirts with Red flash, Blue shorts
Matchday Phone Nº: (020) 8979-2456
Fax Number: (020) 8979-2456
Ground Capacity: 3,500
Seating Capacity: 300
Web site: www.hamptonfc.net

GENERAL INFORMATION

Car Parking: At the ground and street parking
Coach Parking: Contact the Club for information
Nearest Railway Station: Hampton
Nearest Bus Station: Hounslow/Kingston/Fulwell
Club Shop: At the ground
Opening Times: Matchdays only
Telephone Nº: None

GROUND INFORMATION

Away Supporters' Entrances & Sections:
No usual segregation

ADMISSION INFO (2011/2012 PRICES)

Adult Standing: £11.00
Adult Seating: £11.00
Senior Citizen/Concessionary Standing: £6.00
Senior Citizen/Concessionary Seating: £6.00
Under-16s Standing: £3.00
Under-16s Seating: £3.00
Programme Price: £2.50

DISABLED INFORMATION

Wheelchairs: Accommodated
Helpers: Admitted
Prices: Normal prices apply
Disabled Toilets: Available
Contact: (020) 8979-2456 (Bookings are not necessary)

Travelling Supporters' Information:
Routes: From the South: Exit the M3 at Junction 1 and follow the A308 (signposted Kingston). Turn 1st left after Kempton Park into Percy Road. Turn right at the level crossing into Station Road then left into Beaver Close for the ground; From the North: Take the A305 from Twickenham then turn left onto the A311. Pass through Hampton Hill onto Hampton High Street. Turn right at the White Hart pub (just before the junction with the A308), then right into Station Road and right again into Beaver Close.

HAVANT & WATERLOOVILLE FC

Founded: 1998
Former Names: Formed by the amalgamation of Waterlooville FC and Havant Town FC
Nickname: 'The Hawks'
Ground: Westleigh Park, Martin Road, Havant, PO9 5TH
Record Attendance: 5,757 (2006/07)
Pitch Size: 112 × 76 yards

Colours: White shirts and shorts
Telephone Nº: (023) 9278-7822 (Ground)
Fax Number: (023) 9226-2367
Ground Capacity: 5,250
Seating Capacity: 562
Web site: www.havantandwaterlooville.net

GENERAL INFORMATION

Car Parking: Space for 750 cars at the ground
Coach Parking: At the ground
Nearest Railway Station: Havant (1 mile)
Nearest Bus Station: Town Centre (1½ miles)
Club Shop: At the ground
Opening Times: Daily
Telephone Nº: (023) 9278-7822

GROUND INFORMATION

Away Supporters' Entrances & Sections:
Martin Road End

ADMISSION INFO (2011/2012 PRICES)

Adult Standing: £11.00
Adult Seating: £11.00
Senior Citizen Standing/Seating: £6.00
Note: When accompanied by a paying adult, children under the age of 11 are admitted free of charge
Programme Price: £2.00

DISABLED INFORMATION

Wheelchairs: 12 spaces available in the Main Stand
Helpers: Admitted
Prices: Normal prices for disabled fans. Free for helpers
Disabled Toilets: Two available
Contact: (023) 9226-7276 (Bookings are necessary)

Travelling Supporters' Information:
Routes: From London or the North take the A27 from Chichester and exit at the B2149 turn-off for Havant. Take the 2nd exit off the dual carriageway into Bartons Road and then the 1st right into Martin Road for the ground; From the West: Take the M27 then the A27 to the Petersfield exit. Then as above.

MAIDENHEAD UNITED FC

Founded: 1870
Former Names: None
Nickname: 'Magpies'
Ground: York Road, Maidenhead, Berks. SL6 1SF
Record Attendance: 7,920 (1936)
Pitch Size: 110 × 75 yards

Colours: Black and White striped shirts, Black shorts
Telephone Nº: (01628) 636314 (Club)
Contact Number: (01628) 636078
Ground Capacity: 4,500
Seating Capacity: 400
Web: www.pitchero.com/clubs/maidenheadunited/

GENERAL INFORMATION

Car Parking: Street parking
Coach Parking: Street parking
Nearest Railway Station: Maidenhead (¼ mile)
Nearest Bus Station: Maidenhead
Club Shop: At the ground
Opening Times: Matchdays only
Telephone Nº: (01628) 624739

GROUND INFORMATION

Away Supporters' Entrances & Sections:
No usual segregation

ADMISSION INFO (2011/2012 PRICES)

Adult Standing: £10.00
Adult Seating: £10.00
Concessionary Standing and Seating: £6.00
Child Standing and Seating: £2.00 (Under-16s)
Programme Price: £1.00

DISABLED INFORMATION

Wheelchairs: Accommodated
Helpers: Admitted
Prices: Normal prices for the disabled. Free for helpers
Disabled Toilets: Available
Contact: (01628) 636078 (Bookings are not necessary)

Travelling Supporters' Information:
Routes: Exit M4 at Junction 7 and take the A4 to Maidenhead. Cross the River Thames bridge and turn left at the 2nd roundabout passing through the traffic lights. York Road is first right and the ground is approximately 300 yards along on the left.

SALISBURY CITY FC

Founded: 1947
Former Names: Salisbury FC
Nickname: 'The Whites'
Ground: The Raymond McEnhill Stadium, Partridge Way, Old Sarum, Salisbury, Wiltshire SP4 6PU
Record Attendance: 2,633 (19th January 2008)
Pitch Size: 115 × 76 yards

Colours: White shirts and shorts
Telephone Nº: (01722) 776655
Fax Number: (01722) 323100
Ground Capacity: 5,000
Seating Capacity: 500
Web site: www.salisburycity-fc.co.uk

GENERAL INFORMATION

Car Parking: At the ground
Coach Parking: At the ground
Nearest Railway Station: Salisbury (2½ miles)
Nearest Bus Station: Salisbury
Club Shop: At the ground + an online shop
Opening Times: Office Hours and Matchdays
Telephone Nº: (01722) 776655
Postal Sales: Yes

GROUND INFORMATION

Away Supporters' Entrances & Sections:
No usual segregation

ADMISSION INFO (2011/2012 PRICES)

Adult Standing: £9.00
Adult Seating: £10.00
Senior Citizen Standing: £7.00
Senior Citizen Seating: £8.00
Under-16s Standing: £3.00   (Students: £7.00)
Under-16s Seating: £5.00   (Students: £9.00)
Programme Price: £2.50

DISABLED INFORMATION

Wheelchairs: Accommodated in a special area in the Main Stand. A stairlift is available.
Helpers: Admitted free of charge
Prices: Normal prices apply for the disabled
Disabled Toilets: Available
Contact: (01722) 776655   (Bookings are necessary)

Travelling Supporters' Information:
Routes: The Stadium well signposted and is situated off the main A345 Salisbury to Amesbury road on the northern edge of the City, 2 miles from the City Centre.

STAINES TOWN FC

Photograph courtesy of Laurence Wakefield

Founded: 1892
Former Names: Staines FC, Staines Vale FC, Staines Albany FC, Staines Projectile FC & Staines Lagonda FC
Nickname: 'The Swans'
Ground: Wheatsheaf Park, Wheatsheaf Lane, Staines   TW18 2PD
Record Attendance: 2,860 (2007)
Pitch Size: 110 × 76 yards

Ground Capacity: 3,061
Seating Capacity: 500
Colours: Old Gold and Blue shirts with Blue shorts
Telephone Nº: 0782 506-7232
Correspondence Address: Steve Parsons, 3 Birch Green, Staines   TW18 4HA
Web site: www.stainesmassive.co.uk

GENERAL INFORMATION

Car Parking: Large car park shared with The Thames Club
Coach Parking: At the ground
Nearest Railway Station: Staines (1 mile)
Nearest Bus Station: Staines Central (1 mile)
Club Shop: At the ground
Opening Times: Matchdays only
Telephone Nº: (01784) 463100

GROUND INFORMATION

Away Supporters' Entrances & Sections:
No usual segregation

ADMISSION INFO (2011/2012 PRICES)

Adult Standing: £12.00
Adult Seating: £12.00
Senior Citizen Standing/Seating: £6.00
Junior Standing/Seating: £5.00
Programme Price: £2.00

DISABLED INFORMATION

Wheelchairs: Accommodated
Helpers: Admitted
Prices: Normal prices apply for the disabled
Disabled Toilets: Available
Contact: (01784) 225943

Travelling Supporters' Information:
Routes: Exit the M25 at Junction 13 and take the A30 towards London. At the 'Crooked Billet' roundabout follow signs for Staines Town Centre. Pass under the bridge and bear left, passing the Elmsleigh Centre Car Parks and bear left at the next junction (opposite the Thames Lodge Hotel) into Laleham Road. Pass under the iron railway bridge by the river and continue along for ¾ mile. Turn right by the bollards into Wheatsheaf Lane and the ground is situated on the left by the Thames Club.

SUTTON UNITED FC

Founded: 1898
Former Names: Formed by the amalgamation of Sutton Guild Rovers FC and Sutton Association FC
Nickname: 'U's'
Ground: Borough Sports Ground, Gander Green Lane, Sutton, Surrey SM1 2EY
Record Attendance: 14,000 (1970)

Colours: Chocolate and Amber shirts with Chocolate-coloured shorts
Telephone Nº: (020) 8644-4440
Fax Number: (020) 8644-5120
Ground Capacity: 7,032
Seating Capacity: 765
Web site: www.suttonunited.net

GENERAL INFORMATION

Car Parking: 150 spaces behind the Main Stand
Coach Parking: Space for 1 coach in the car park
Nearest Railway Station: West Sutton (adjacent)
Club Shop: At the ground
Opening Times: Matchdays only
Telephone Nº: (020) 8644-4440

GROUND INFORMATION

Away Supporters' Entrances & Sections:
Collingwood Road entrances and accommodation

ADMISSION INFO (2011/2012 PRICES)

Adult Standing: £11.00
Adult Seating: £12.00
Child Standing: £2.00
Child Seating: £3.00
Senior Citizen Standing: £6.00
Senior Citizen Seating: £7.00
Programme Price: £2.50

DISABLED INFORMATION

Wheelchairs: 8 spaces are available under cover accommodated on the track perimeter
Helpers: Admitted
Prices: Normal prices apply
Disabled Toilets: Available alongside the Standing Terrace
Contact: (020) 8644-4440 (Bookings are necessary)

Travelling Supporters' Information:
Routes: Exit the M25 at Junction 8 (Reigate Hill) and travel North on the A217 for approximately 8 miles. Cross the A232 then turn right at the traffic lights (past Goose & Granit Public House) into Gander Green Lane. The ground is 300 yards on the left; From London: Gander Green Lane crosses the Sutton bypass 1 mile south of Rose Hill Roundabout. Avoid Sutton Town Centre, especially on Saturdays.

THURROCK FC

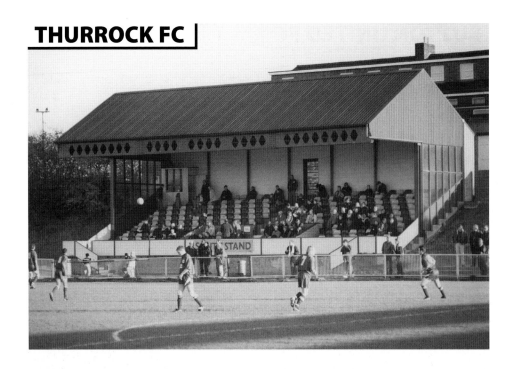

Founded: 1985
Former Names: Purfleet FC
Nickname: 'Fleet'
Ground: Thurrock Hotel, Ship Lane, Grays, Essex, RM19 1YN   **Telephone Nº**: (01708) 865492
Record Attendance: 2,572 (1998)
Pitch Size: 113 × 72 yards

Colours: Yellow and Green shirts with Green shorts
Tel Nº: (01708) 865492 (Clubhouse)
Contact Nº: 07979 525117 (Secretary)
Fax Number: (01708) 868863
Ground Capacity: 4,200
Seating Capacity: 500
Web site: www.thurrock-fc.com

GENERAL INFORMATION

Car Parking: At the ground
Coach Parking: At the ground
Nearest Railway Station: Purfleet (2 miles)
Nearest Bus Station: Grays Town Centre
Club Shop: At the ground
Opening Times: Matchdays only
Telephone Nº: (01708) 865492

GROUND INFORMATION

Away Supporters' Entrances & Sections:
No usual segregation

ADMISSION INFO (2011/2012 PRICES)

Adult Standing: £12.00
Adult Seating: £12.00
Child Standing: £3.00
Child Seating: £3.00
Senior Citizen Standing: £8.00
Senior Citizen Seating: £8.00
Programme Price: £2.00

DISABLED INFORMATION

Wheelchairs: No special area but accommodated
Helpers: Admitted
Prices: Free for the disabled. Helpers pay normal prices
Disabled Toilets: Available in the Clubhouse
Contact: (01708) 865492 (Bookings are not necessary)

Travelling Supporters' Information:
Routes: Take the M25 or A13 to the Dartford Tunnel roundabout. The ground is then 50 yards on the right along Ship Lane.

TONBRIDGE ANGELS FC

Founded: 1948
Former Names: Tonbridge FC
Nickname: 'The Angels'
Ground: Longmead Stadium, Darenth Avenue, Tonbridge TN10 3JF
Record Attendance: 2,281 (2008)

Colours: Blue and White shirts with Blue shorts
Telephone Nº: (01732) 352417
Ground Capacity: 2,500
Seating Capacity: 720
Web site: www.tonbridgeangels.co.uk

GENERAL INFORMATION

Car Parking: At the ground
Coach Parking: At the ground
Nearest Railway Station: Tonbridge (2 miles)
Club Shop: At the ground
Opening Times: Matchdays only
Telephone Nº: (01732) 352417

GROUND INFORMATION

Away Supporters' Entrances & Sections:
No usual segregation

ADMISSION INFO (2011/2012 PRICES)

Adult Standing: £12.00
Adult Seating: £12.00
Student/Senior Citizen Standing: £6.00
Student/Senior Citizen Seating: £6.00
Under-12s Standing: £3.00
Under-12s Seating: £3.00
Programme Price: £2.00

DISABLED INFORMATION

Wheelchairs: Accommodated
Helpers: Admitted
Prices: Normal prices apply
Disabled Toilets: One available
Contact: (01732) 352417

Travelling Supporters' Information:
Routes: Take the A26 or A21 to Tonbridge Town Centre, pass through the High Street and head north up Shipbourne Road which is the A227 Gravesend road. Turn left at the 2nd mini-roundabout by the 'Pinnacles' Pub into Darenth Avenue. The ground is situated at the bottom end of Darenth Avenue.

TRURO CITY FC

Founded: 1889
Former Names: None
Nickname: 'White Tigers'
Ground: Treyew Road, Truro TR1 2TH
Record Attendance: 2,637 (31st March 2007)

Colours: All White shirts and shorts
Telephone Nº: (01872) 225400
Fax Number: (01872) 225402
Ground Capacity: 3,000
Seating Capacity: 1,600
Web Site: www.trurocityfc.co.uk

GENERAL INFORMATION

Car Parking: At the ground
Coach Parking: At the ground
Nearest Railway Station: Truro (½ mile)
Club Shop: None

GROUND INFORMATION

Away Supporters' Entrances & Sections:
No usual segregation

ADMISSION INFO (2011/2012 PRICES)

Adult Standing/Seating: £10.00
Senior Citizen Standing/Seating: £7.00
Under-16s Standing/Seating: £3.00
Under-12s Standing/Seating: Free of charge
Programme Price: £2.50

DISABLED INFORMATION

Wheelchairs: Accommodated
Helpers: Admitted
Prices: Normal prices apply for the disabled and helpers
Disabled Toilets: Available
Contact: (01872) 225400 (Bookings are not necessary)

Travelling Supporters' Information:
Routes: From the North or East: Take the A30 to the A390 (from the North) or travel straight on the A390 (from the East) to Truro. Continue on the A390 and pass through Truro. The ground is located just to the South West of Truro on the left hand side of the A390 just before the County Hall; From the West: Take the A390 to Truro. The ground is on the right hand side of the road shortly after crossing the railway line and passing the County Hall; From the South: Take the A39 to Truro. At the junction with the A390 turn left onto Green Lane and the ground is on the left hand side of the road after approximately ½ mile.

WELLING UNITED FC

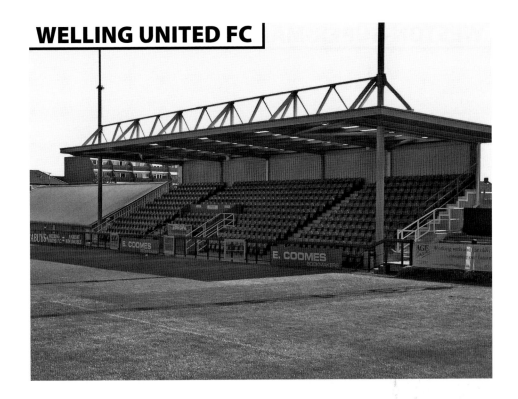

Founded: 1963
Former Names: None
Nickname: 'The Wings'
Ground: Park View Road Ground, Welling, Kent, DA16 1SY
Record Attendance: 4,020 (1989/90)
Pitch Size: 112 × 72 yards

Colours: Shirts are Red with White facings, Red shorts
Telephone Nº: (0208) 301-1196
Daytime Phone Nº: (0208) 301-1196
Fax Number: (0208) 301-5676
Ground Capacity: 4,000
Seating Capacity: 500
Web site: www.wellingunited.com

GENERAL INFORMATION

Car Parking: Street parking only
Coach Parking: Outside of the ground
Nearest Railway Station: Welling (¾ mile)
Nearest Bus Station: Bexleyheath
Club Shop: At the ground
Opening Times: Matchdays only
Telephone Nº: (0208) 301-1196

GROUND INFORMATION

Away Supporters' Entrances & Sections:
Accommodation in the Danson Park End

ADMISSION INFO (2011/2012 PRICES)

Adult Standing: £12.00
Adult Seating: £13.00
Senior Citizen/Child Standing: £7.00
Senior Citizen/Child Seating: £8.00
Under-12s: £3.00
Programme Price: £2.00

DISABLED INFORMATION

Wheelchairs: Accommodated at the side of the Main Stand
Helpers: Admitted
Prices: £6.00 for the disabled. Helpers pay normal prices
Disabled Toilets: Yes
Contact: (0208) 301-1196   (Bookings are not necessary)

Travelling Supporters' Information:
Routes: Take the A2 (Rochester Way) from London, then the A221 Northwards (Danson Road) to Bexleyheath. At the end turn left towards Welling along Park View Road and the ground is on the left.

WESTON-SUPER-MARE FC

Founded: 1899
Former Names: Christ Church Old Boys FC
Nickname: 'Seagulls'
Ground: Woodspring Stadium, Winterstoke Road, Weston-super-Mare BS24 9AA
Record Attendance: 2,623 (vs Woking in F.A. Cup)
Pitch Size: 110 × 70 yards

Colours: White shirts with Black shorts
Telephone Nº: (01934) 621618
Fax Number: (01934) 622704
Ground Capacity: 3,071
Seating Capacity: 320
Web site: www.weston-s-mareafc.co.uk

GENERAL INFORMATION
Car Parking: 140 spaces available at the ground
Coach Parking: At the ground
Nearest Railway Station: Weston-super-Mare (1½ miles)
Nearest Bus Station: Weston-super-Mare (1½ miles)
Club Shop: At the ground
Opening Times: Matchdays only
Telephone Nº: (01934) 621618

GROUND INFORMATION
Away Supporters' Entrances & Sections:
No usual segregation

ADMISSION INFO (2011/2012 PRICES)
Adult Standing/Seating: £10.00
Senior Citizen Standing/Seating: £6.00
Under-16s Standing/Seating: £6.00
Note: Under-10s are admitted for £1.00 when accompanied by a paying adult or senior citizen
Programme Price: £2.00

DISABLED INFORMATION
Wheelchairs: Accommodated in a special disabled section
Helpers: Admitted
Prices: Normal prices apply
Disabled Toilets: Two available
Contact: (01934) 621618   (Bookings are not necessary)

Travelling Supporters' Information:
Routes: Exit the M5 at Junction 21 and follow the dual carriageway (A370) to the 4th roundabout (Asda Winterstoke). Turn left, go over the mini-roundabout and continue for 800 yards. The ground is on the right.

WOKING FC

Founded: 1889
Former Names: None
Nickname: 'Cardinals'
Ground: Kingfield Stadium, Kingfield, Woking, Surrey   GU22 9AA
Record Attendance: 6,000 (1997)
Pitch Size: 109 × 76 yards

Colours: Shirts are Red & White halves, Black shorts
Telephone N°: (01483) 772470
Daytime Phone N°: (01483) 772470
Fax Number: (01483) 888423
Ground Capacity: 6,161
Seating Capacity: 2,511
Web site: www.wokingfc.co.uk

GENERAL INFORMATION

Car Parking: Limited parking at the ground
Coach Parking: At or opposite the ground
Nearest Railway Station: Woking (1 mile)
Nearest Bus Station: Woking
Club Shop: At the ground
Opening Times: Weekdays and Matchdays
Telephone N°: (01483) 772470

GROUND INFORMATION

Away Supporters' Entrances & Sections:
Kingfield Road entrance for the Tennis Club terrace

ADMISSION INFO (2011/2012 PRICES)

Adult Standing: £12.00
Adult Seating: £12.00
Under-16s/Student Standing: £2.00
Under-16s/Student Seating: £2.00
Senior Citizen Standing: £8.00
Senior Citizen Seating: £8.00
Programme Price: £2.50

DISABLED INFORMATION

Wheelchairs: 8 spaces in the Leslie Gosden Stand and 8 spaces in front of the Family Stand
Helpers: Admitted
Prices: One wheelchair and helper for £8.00
Disabled Toilets: Yes – in the Leslie Gosden Stand and Family Stand area
Contact: (01483) 772470   (Bookings are necessary)

Travelling Supporters' Information:
Routes: Exit the M25 at Junction 10 and follow the A3 towards Guildford. Leave at the next junction onto the B2215 through Ripley and join the A247 to Woking. Alternatively, exit the M25 at Junction 11 and follow the A320 to Woking Town Centre. The ground is on the outskirts of Woking – follow signs on the A320 and A247.

Blue Square Premier 2010/2011 Season

	AFC Wimbledon	Altrincham	Barrow	Bath City	Cambridge United	Crawley Town	Darlington	Eastbourne Borough	Fleetwood Town	Forest Green Rovers	Gateshead	Grimsby Town	Hayes & Yeading	Histon	Kettering Town	Kidderminster Harriers	Luton Town	Mansfield Town	Newport County	Rushden & Diamonds	Southport	Tamworth	Wrexham	York City
AFC Wimbledon	■	4-1	2-0	4-0	3-0	2-1	0-2	3-0	1-0	1-1	1-0	2-1	3-1	2-0	3-2	1-2	0-0	2-1	2-2	1-0	5-0	3-0	0-1	1-0
Altrincham	0-2	■	2-0	0-3	2-2	0-1	2-2	3-4	1-0	2-1	1-1	2-2	4-2	0-3	3-2	1-2	0-1	0-4	1-3	2-2	1-1	2-0	0-0	0-0
Barrow	2-0	1-0	■	0-1	1-2	1-1	1-1	4-0	0-2	3-0	1-3	0-2	2-0	1-1	5-0	2-1	0-1	2-2	2-1	2-0	1-1	0-2	0-1	0-0
Bath City	2-2	2-2	1-1	■	4-0	0-2	2-2	1-1	1-1	2-4	1-0	2-1	3-1	2-1	1-1	2-0	0-0	2-0	2-2	2-1	2-1	2-0	0-2	2-2
Cambridge United	1-2	4-0	3-1	1-2	■	2-2	0-1	2-0	0-1	1-1	5-0	1-1	1-0	0-0	3-0	1-2	0-0	1-5	0-1	0-2	0-0	3-3	1-3	2-1
Crawley Town	3-1	7-0	3-2	2-1	3-0	■	1-0	3-1	1-1	1-0	2-1	0-1	5-2	5-0	2-1	2-0	1-1	2-0	2-3	4-0	1-0	3-1	3-2	1-1
Darlington	0-0	0-1	3-1	3-1	1-0	1-1	■	6-1	4-0	3-0	2-0	0-1	0-1	3-1	1-1	1-1	2-2	0-0	1-0	2-0	1-0	1-0	0-1	2-1
Eastbourne Borough	2-3	5-0	0-2	2-0	0-2	1-2	1-1	■	0-6	0-0	2-3	5-0	2-2	1-3	1-1	2-4	1-3	0-0	0-2	4-1	1-4	4-3	2-1	2-1
Fleetwood Town	1-1	3-1	1-0	2-1	2-2	1-2	1-0	0-1	■	2-0	0-0	3-0	1-1	1-1	4-1	1-1	0-3	1-1	1-1	2-0	2-1	1-0	2-1	2-1
Forest Green Rovers	0-0	1-0	2-3	0-0	1-1	0-3	1-1	3-4	1-0	■	1-1	3-3	1-0	0-1	0-2	1-1	0-1	2-1	0-0	2-2	0-0	4-0	3-0	2-1
Gateshead	0-2	2-0	3-0	1-2	2-3	0-0	2-2	3-0	0-2	1-1	■	0-0	1-0	0-0	2-2	1-0	1-1	1-7	2-2	1-0	3-1	0-1	0-1	0-3
Grimsby Town	2-1	0-1	1-1	2-2	1-1	0-0	0-1	2-2	1-2	1-1	2-2	■	1-2	2-1	3-3	2-0	7-2	1-1	1-1	2-2	2-1	2-2	2-1	0-0
Hayes & Yeading United	0-0	3-0	2-0	2-1	2-0	0-3	3-2	2-1	1-2	3-4	3-1	0-3	■	1-2	3-2	0-4	0-1	4-0	1-2	3-3	1-0	2-1	0-3	1-2
Histon	0-4	3-0	3-1	1-2	0-2	0-2	0-1	1-1	1-0	0-3	1-3	1-6	0-1	■	0-3	0-1	0-4	2-3	0-0	0-2	2-1	1-2	1-1	1-2
Kettering Town	1-2	3-3	1-1	2-1	2-2	0-0	0-0	3-0	2-1	2-1	1-4	1-2	2-1	4-3	■	1-1	1-3	0-2	2-0	0-1	3-1	0-1	1-1	1-1
Kidderminster Harriers	2-0	2-1	2-0	1-0	0-0	0-0	1-2	2-1	1-0	2-1	2-1	3-2	3-1	2-2	4-1	■	3-3	1-3	2-3	1-0	3-4	2-2	1-0	0-0
Luton Town	3-0	2-1	0-0	3-1	2-0	1-2	4-0	3-0	1-3	6-1	2-2	1-0	1-1	5-1	2-2	1-1	■	2-0	1-1	3-0	6-0	2-0	1-1	5-0
Mansfield Town	2-5	0-1	1-1	2-0	1-0	1-4	1-1	4-0	2-5	3-1	3-2	0-2	3-2	1-0	1-1	1-2	0-0	■	3-3	2-1	2-2	0-1	2-3	5-0
Newport County	3-3	2-1	5-0	1-2	1-1	0-1	2-1	3-3	1-3	3-1	2-1	2-1	2-2	1-2	3-0	1-1	1-0	1-3	■	2-0	1-1	1-1	1-1	4-0
Rushden & Diamonds	1-0	1-2	5-0	5-1	2-1	0-1	2-1	2-0	1-1	2-2	0-2	4-1	1-1	2-0	1-2	2-1	0-1	1-0	0-1	■	2-2	1-1	2-2	0-4
Southport	0-1	1-0	2-4	2-3	1-1	0-4	1-1	1-3	1-0	4-0	5-1	2-2	0-0	3-1	1-2	2-2	2-1	1-2	2-1	2-2	■	2-1	0-1	4-0
Tamworth	2-5	1-0	2-2	2-2	1-1	0-3	1-1	4-2	0-2	2-1	1-1	2-1	2-3	0-1	3-1	2-2	3-1	0-2	3-2	1-2	0-1	■	1-1	1-3
Wrexham	1-2	2-1	1-1	2-0	1-0	0-0	2-1	2-1	0-0	2-1	2-7	2-0	0-2	4-0	2-0	2-2	1-0	1-1	1-0	1-1	2-1	4-2	■	1-1
York City	4-1	3-0	0-0	1-1	0-0	1-1	0-0	1-0	1-0	2-1	2-1	1-0	2-0	1-0	0-1	1-2	1-0	2-1	2-1	2-0	2-0	1-2	1-1	■

Blue Square Premier (Football Conference)

Season 2010/2011

Team	P	W	D	L	F	A	Pts
Crawley Town	46	31	12	3	93	30	105
AFC Wimbledon	46	27	9	10	83	47	90
Luton Town	46	23	15	8	85	37	84
Wrexham	46	22	15	9	66	49	81
Fleetwood Town	46	22	12	12	68	42	78
Kidderminster Harriers	46	20	17	9	74	60	72
Darlington	46	18	17	11	61	42	71
York City	46	19	14	13	55	50	71
Newport County	46	18	15	13	78	60	69
Bath City	46	16	15	15	64	68	63
Grimsby Town	46	15	17	14	72	62	62
Mansfield Town	46	17	10	19	73	75	61
Rushden & Diamonds	46	16	14	16	65	62	57
Gateshead	46	14	15	17	65	68	57
Kettering Town	46	15	13	18	64	75	56
Hayes & Yeading United	46	15	6	25	57	81	51
Cambridge United	46	11	17	18	53	61	50
Barrow	46	12	14	20	52	67	50
Tamworth	46	12	13	21	62	83	49
Forest Green Rovers	46	10	16	20	53	72	46
Southport	46	11	13	22	56	77	46
Altrincham	46	11	11	24	47	87	44
Eastbourne Borough	46	10	9	27	62	104	39
Histon	46	8	9	29	41	90	28

Kidderminster Harriers, Histon and Rushden & Diamonds each had 5 points deducted.

Rushden & Diamonds were subsequently expelled from the Football Conference on 11th June 2011.

Kettering Town had two points deducted.

Promotion Play-offs

Fleetwood Town	0	AFC Wimbledon	2
Wrexham	0	Luton Town	3
AFC Wimbledon	6	Fleetwood Town	1

AFC Wimbledon won 8-1 on aggregate

Luton Town	2	Wrexham	1

Luton Town won 5-1 on aggregate

AFC Wimbledon	0	Luton Town	0 (aet.)

AFC Wimbledon won 4-3 on penalties

Promoted: Crawley Town and AFC Wimbledon
Relegated: Altrincham, Eastbourne Borough and Histon

Blue Square North 2010/2011 Season

	AFC Telford United	Alfreton Town	Blyth Spartans	Boston United	Corby Town	Droylsden	Eastwood Town	Gainsborough Trinity	Gloucester City	Guiseley	Harrogate Town	Hinckley United	Hyde	Ilkeston Town	Nuneaton Town	Redditch United	Solihull Moors	Stafford Rangers	Stalybridge Celtic	Vauxhall Motors	Worcester City	Workington
AFC Telford United		2-1	1-1	0-1	5-0	1-1	2-2	2-1	2-0	1-0	3-0	2-2	5-0		4-1	3-1	2-4	0-0	1-0	4-1	1-1	1-0
Alfreton Town	0-0		2-1	0-1	6-0	4-0	2-2	2-1	4-0	6-0	6-0	1-0	0-0		3-2	4-0	2-0	2-0	5-3	2-0	2-1	2-0
Blyth Spartans	3-0	1-4		0-0	1-1	2-4	0-0	1-3	0-2	0-0	1-0	4-0	3-0		1-0	2-0	0-1	3-2	1-2	2-2	3-0	2-1
Boston United	0-1	3-2	5-0		1-0	2-0	1-0	1-3	1-0	1-1	2-2	3-0	2-2		1-2	1-0	1-1	1-0	1-0	2-0	1-0	4-0
Corby Town	0-0	0-1	3-4	0-0		1-0	1-6	3-1	0-2	2-2	2-1	2-0	1-2		2-3	3-2	0-2	1-3	2-2	3-1	1-1	1-0
Droylsden	2-4	2-1	0-3	4-0	1-1		4-2	1-1	2-4	0-3	5-1	3-2	3-1		1-0	3-0	0-5	2-0	2-2	1-3	2-1	3-0
Eastwood Town	3-0	4-2	0-2	2-2	2-1	2-0		2-0	1-2	0-1	2-0	6-2	1-0		2-1	2-1	2-1	3-0	1-1	3-1	2-4	0-2
Gainsborough Trinity	0-5	0-3	0-2	0-3	3-1	0-3	1-3		2-0	1-3	1-3	0-1	2-1		1-2	3-0	1-1	2-2	1-3	1-1	0-2	1-1
Gloucester City	2-2	2-1	1-2	0-1	0-2	1-1	1-3	0-2		1-2	3-2	2-1	1-0		0-3	5-0	2-4	1-2	0-2	1-0	1-1	2-0
Guiseley	0-3	1-2	0-0	0-0	4-0	2-1	2-2	2-0	1-1		1-0	3-2	1-0		1-2	3-1	1-0	1-1	3-1	1-2	0-1	2-2
Harrogate Town	0-0	1-1	2-2	3-6	0-1	3-3	2-1	3-1	3-0	0-0		2-2	1-3		1-2	3-0	2-0	3-2	2-0	0-0	1-0	2-0
Hinckley United	1-1	1-3	5-1	0-1	3-3	1-1	2-3	3-1	3-0	1-2	4-0		2-0		0-3	4-0	2-2	4-0	5-2	2-3	3-1	1-2
Hyde	0-3	1-5	0-2	0-3	2-1	1-1	1-2	1-1	1-3	0-1	1-0	3-0			1-1	1-4	1-2	1-0	0-2	1-2	0-2	2-3
Ilkeston Town																						
Nuneaton Town	0-0	1-3	3-2	1-1	2-3	1-1	2-1	1-2	0-0	3-0	2-0	1-2				1-1	2-1	1-0	2-1	3-0	2-1	2-1
Redditch United	1-1	1-5	2-1	0-9	2-2	1-3	0-6	1-4	0-1	2-3	0-1	2-3	0-1		0-5		0-0	0-1	1-3	2-2	0-0	1-1
Solihull Moors	0-1	0-1	2-0	1-0	7-2	2-2	2-0	0-2	2-1		2-2	2-7	3-2		1-1	3-0		1-1	3-1	1-0	2-0	2-0
Stafford Rangers	0-2	0-1	2-1	0-4	3-5	1-5	0-2	3-1	0-2	2-2	1-1	1-3	0-5		1-2	2-1	1-0		1-3	1-0	1-1	0-2
Stalybridge Celtic	0-1	1-2	0-0	3-1	1-1	4-0	2-1	2-0	4-3	0-0	0-1	1-1	1-2		0-2	2-0	1-1	3-2		1-3	0-0	0-2
Vauxhall Motors	0-1	0-2	2-6	0-0	3-2	0-1	1-2	1-0	2-1	2-2	1-1	2-0	3-2		1-1	2-1	3-3	2-1	0-3		2-3	1-2
Worcester City	0-3	1-2	1-0	2-0	0-2	0-1	1-1	1-2	2-0	1-2	2-3	3-2	4-2		2-2	1-1	0-1	2-2	1-0	4-1		1-2
Workington	0-1	0-0	1-1	3-5	1-2	2-0	0-3	4-2	2-1	0-1	2-1	3-1	1-1		0-1	5-1	2-1	2-0	0-5	2-1	2-0	

Blue Square North (Football Conference)

Season 2010/2011

Alfreton Town	40	29	5	6	97	33	92
AFC Telford United	40	23	13	4	71	29	82
Boston United	40	23	10	7	72	33	79
Eastwood Town	40	22	7	11	82	50	73
Guiseley	40	20	13	7	56	41	73
Nuneaton Town	40	21	9	10	66	44	72
Solihull Moors	40	18	10	12	66	49	64
Droylsden	40	17	9	14	69	67	60
Blyth Spartans	40	16	10	14	61	54	58
Stalybridge Celtic	40	16	9	15	64	55	57
Workington	40	16	6	18	52	60	54
Harrogate Town	40	13	11	16	53	66	50
Corby Town	40	13	10	17	58	80	49
Gloucester City	40	14	5	21	49	63	47
Hinckley United	40	13	7	20	76	76	46
Worcester City	40	12	10	18	49	55	46
Vauxhall Motors	40	12	9	19	52	71	45
Gainsborough Trinity	40	12	5	23	50	74	41
Hyde	40	10	6	24	44	73	36
Stafford Rangers	40	8	8	24	39	78	32
Redditch United	40	2	8	30	30	105	9

Redditch United had 5 points deducted.
Eastwood Town were deemed ineligible for promotion or participation in the play-offs due to ground grading issues.
Ilkeston Town were wound-up on 8th September 2010 and the club was expelled from the league on 15th September 2010.
Their record was expunged: 7   1   3   3   7   13   7

Promotion Play-offs North

Nuneaton Town 1	Fleetwood Town 1
Guiseley 1	Boston United 0

AFC Telford United 2   Nuneaton Town 1
AFC Telford United won 3-2 on aggregate

Boston United 3   Guiseley .... 2 (aet.)
Aggregate 3-3. Guiseley won 3-2 on penalties

AFC Telford United 3   Guiseley 2

Promoted: Alfreton Town and AFC Telford United

Relegated: Stafford Rangers and Redditch United

Blue Square South — 2010/2011 Season

	Basingstoke Town	Bishop's Stortford	Boreham Wood	Braintree Town	Bromley	Chelmsford City	Dartford	Dorchester Town	Dover Athletic	Eastleigh	Ebbsfleet United	Farnborough	Hampton & Richmond Borough	Havant & Waterlooville	Lewes	Maidenhead United	St Albans City	Staines Town	Thurrock	Welling United	Weston-super-Mare	Woking
Basingstoke Town		0-1	1-0	0-2	4-1	2-3	2-2	1-0	3-2	1-2	1-2	1-0	4-0	0-2	1-1	3-4	0-2	4-1	2-2	1-3	2-2	1-0
Bishop's Stortford	0-2		2-0	1-2	0-1	2-2	0-1	2-1	1-4	0-1	0-3	1-4	0-2	1-5	1-0	0-0	4-0	2-1	1-0	0-4	1-1	0-4
Boreham Wood	1-0	1-2		0-2	2-4	2-0	3-1	0-0	2-3	2-1	0-1	2-4	2-2	1-0	3-0	4-2	0-3	2-2	2-2	0-1	6-3	0-0
Braintree Town	5-2	3-1	3-2		0-2	3-0	1-1	1-1	1-2	1-0	4-1	3-0	3-1	2-0	1-0	3-1	1-1	0-0	1-0	3-1	4-0	2-0
Bromley	0-1	4-3	1-1	0-3		0-3	4-1	2-1	0-2	0-2	1-1	0-0	1-2	1-0	1-1	0-2	1-1	0-1	1-0	2-1	3-2	2-2
Chelmsford City	4-0	4-1	3-1	0-0	2-0		2-0	2-0	2-2	3-0	2-3	0-1	3-1	1-2	4-0	2-0	1-1	3-1	6-1	0-2	1-0	3-0
Dartford	1-0	3-0	1-4	1-0	2-2	1-2		0-4	4-0	0-0	1-1	4-1	0-4	2-2	3-0	3-0	2-2	1-1	0-1	1-1	4-1	3-2
Dorchester Town	0-1	0-0	3-1	1-0	0-0	1-1	0-2		0-0	0-4	1-2	2-1	2-2	0-0	0-0	1-2	1-3	3-3	3-1	3-3	1-0	1-2
Dover Athletic	3-0	2-0	1-0	1-2	1-1	2-3	0-2	2-1		0-1	1-3	6-3	1-0	0-0	4-0	2-2	4-1	1-1	1-0	2-2	0-1	2-2
Eastleigh	0-1	1-2	3-0	0-2	1-0	2-1	3-0	3-0	0-2		0-3	0-3	3-0	4-2	2-1	3-0	4-2	1-4	3-1	1-4	1-1	4-1
Ebbsfleet United	3-1	0-0	2-2	0-0	1-2	1-3	2-1	3-2	0-2	2-2		0-3	1-0	2-1	1-0	1-2	4-0	1-1	2-2	4-0	3-1	1-1
Farnborough	1-1	3-2	0-1	2-1	2-2	3-1	2-1	0-0	4-1	1-2	1-2		2-0	2-0	1-0	2-2	1-0	0-0	3-2	2-2	2-0	1-2
Hampton & Richmond Borough	2-2	0-3	0-0	0-1	1-2	3-0	1-0	2-2	3-2	2-2	2-4	0-4		0-1	1-2	1-1	0-0	0-0	0-0	0-1	0-1	1-2
Havant & Waterlooville	2-0	4-1	2-1	1-2	2-0	1-2	1-0	3-1	0-0	2-2	2-3	0-3	1-2		1-2	2-1	0-1	1-1	4-1	1-3	0-0	1-1
Lewes	0-0	1-2	2-2	2-1	0-0	0-1	1-1	0-2	0-3	1-4	0-3	1-5	1-2	2-1		1-0	3-1	0-1	2-1	1-3	1-1	0-4
Maidenhead United	1-1	2-2	1-1	0-3	0-2	1-2	2-3	1-1	0-1	1-0	1-1	0-3	0-0	0-1	0-2		2-1	2-3	1-3	0-3	1-0	0-1
St Albans City	0-0	1-4	0-1	0-0	1-1	0-2	1-2	1-4	1-5	0-1	1-2	0-2	1-1	1-1	0-0	1-0		2-0	0-2	1-0	3-4	0-1
Staines Town	1-1	3-0	0-0	4-4	0-2	2-1	2-0	1-2	1-0	0-5	0-2	1-2	1-2	0-1	1-0	1-2	2-2		1-1	1-2	2-1	1-0
Thurrock	0-3	1-3	1-3	0-3	1-2	1-1	1-1	1-1	2-7	2-1	0-0	2-4	2-2	1-1	3-1	1-2	2-2	2-1		2-1	3-0	0-1
Welling United	4-0	3-1	3-1	1-3	3-1	3-2	2-1	1-2	0-1	4-2	1-1	1-0	0-0	0-2	2-1	2-1	6-0	4-0	1-1		1-0	2-0
Weston-super-Mare	1-0	3-1	2-0	2-1	7-0	2-2	0-1	1-0	1-4	0-2	3-2	0-2	0-0	1-1	0-3	3-1	2-1	2-1	2-1	2-0		0-1
Woking	2-0	2-0	3-0	0-1	1-0	2-2	2-2	2-1	0-1	1-1	3-0	1-2	2-1	3-1	2-1	0-2	2-0	2-0	1-0	0-0	4-3	

Blue Square South (Football Conference)

Season 2010/2011

Braintree Town	42	27	8	7	78	33	89
Farnborough	42	25	7	10	83	47	82
Ebbsfleet United	42	22	12	8	75	51	78
Chelmsford City	42	23	8	11	82	50	77
Woking	42	22	10	10	63	42	76
Welling United	42	24	8	10	81	47	75
Dover Athletic	42	22	8	12	80	51	74
Eastleigh	42	22	6	14	74	53	72
Havant & Waterlooville	42	16	10	16	56	51	58
Dartford	42	15	12	15	60	59	57
Bromley	42	15	12	15	49	61	57
Weston-super-Mare	42	15	8	19	56	67	53
Basingstoke Town	42	13	10	19	50	63	49
Boreham Wood	42	12	11	19	56	67	47
Staines Town	42	11	14	17	48	63	47
Bishop's Stortford	42	13	6	23	48	79	45
Dorchester Town	42	10	14	18	49	59	44
Hampton & Richmond Borough	42	9	15	18	43	61	42
Maidenhead United	42	10	10	22	43	70	40
Thurrock	42	8	13	21	50	77	37
Lewes	42	9	9	24	34	70	36
St. Albans City	42	7	13	22	39	75	24

St. Albans City had 10 points deducted.
Welling United had 5 points deducted.

Promotion Play-offs South

Woking 0   Farnborough 1
Chelmsford City 1   Ebbsfleet United 4

Farnborough 1   Woking .... 1 (aet.)
Farnborough won 2-1 on aggregate
Ebbsfleet United 2   Chelmsford City 1
Ebbsfleet United won 6-2 on aggregate

Farnborough 2   Ebbsfleet United 4

Promoted: Braintree Town and Ebbsfleet United
Relegated: Lewes and St. Albans City

Evo-Stik League Premier Division
2010/2011 Season

	Ashton United	Bradford Park Avenue	Burscough	Buxton	Chasetown	Colwyn Bay	FC Halifax Town	FC United of Manchester	Frickley Athletic	Hucknall Town	Kendal Town	Marine	Matlock Town	Mickleover Sports	Nantwich Town	North Ferriby United	Northwich Victoria	Ossett Town	Retford United	Stocksbridge Park Steels	Whitby Town	Worksop Town
Ashton United		1-3	1-0	2-1	2-3	3-0	0-3	1-0	3-6	4-0	1-2	1-0	3-1	2-3	2-4	0-1	2-1	0-1	1-0	3-1	1-3	3-1
Bradford Park Avenue	2-0		3-1	4-1	2-1	1-4	1-3	4-1	2-3	6-0	5-2	2-1	3-1	1-0	1-0	1-2	2-2	0-1	2-0	3-0	1-1	4-0
Burscough	4-1	2-3		1-2	0-3	0-0	0-2	0-2	3-0	3-0	2-4	1-2	0-3	3-2	3-1	2-2	0-0	0-1	0-1	0-2	1-0	3-1
Buxton	1-1	1-1	1-0		2-0	0-0	2-1	2-2	7-1	4-0	3-0	2-1	1-3	1-2	2-1	0-0	2-2	2-0	7-0	0-0	2-0	0-1
Chasetown	2-1	5-0	5-0	0-1		2-2	2-1	2-0	2-0	1-0	0-1	0-1	2-1	2-3	2-2	2-2	1-0	1-0	6-0	0-2	1-1	2-6
Colwyn Bay	0-3	2-2	2-1	2-1	1-0		2-1	3-1	4-0	2-0	2-1	0-3	0-1	1-1	2-0	0-2	0-6	3-1	1-0	3-4	2-0	2-1
FC Halifax Town	1-0	1-0	3-2	2-1	3-2	1-1		4-1	3-1	4-0	3-0	1-0	2-2	1-1	3-1	0-2	1-1	8-1	3-0	5-1	5-1	0-0
FC United of Manchester	2-1	2-0	3-1	1-2	4-2	0-1	0-1		4-1	4-1	1-2	2-1	1-5	0-0	1-0	2-0	1-0	4-1	5-1	1-4	4-0	2-1
Frickley Athletic	0-0	2-2	0-1	2-2	2-1	0-1	0-0	0-0		1-0	0-2	2-3	0-1	1-0	3-0	0-1	2-1	0-1	1-2	1-1	0-0	1-0
Hucknall Town	0-0	2-2	2-2	0-1	2-2	0-1	1-2	1-2	2-0		4-3	0-3	2-2	1-0	3-1	3-2	0-2	3-3	5-3	2-2	1-2	1-2
Kendal Town	1-0	4-1	1-2	1-1	4-0	1-4	2-4	3-2	1-0	0-0		2-1	1-0	1-2	2-1	2-5	1-1	5-4	4-1	2-3	2-1	2-1
Marine	4-0	1-0	2-2	1-2	2-1	1-3	0-6	0-2	1-1	1-1	2-0		2-4	1-2	4-3	2-3	3-1	4-3	2-0	5-4	1-3	2-4
Matlock Town	1-1	0-1	2-1	1-3	3-4	3-0	1-2	1-2	1-0	1-2	3-1	0-1		1-2	4-2	2-1	1-1	2-0	4-2	1-0	2-2	1-0
Mickleover Sports	0-1	1-3	2-1	2-4	1-3	4-0	2-3	2-0	3-0	1-1	1-3	0-0	1-0		6-6	3-4	2-3	2-4	4-1	2-0	2-4	0-1
Nantwich Town	0-2	0-1	3-2	1-1	0-4	2-1	0-6	1-4	4-3	1-2	5-3	1-1	2-3	0-0		2-1	2-1	2-1	1-0	4-2	3-1	1-2
North Ferriby United	3-2	1-2	2-1	2-0	0-1	1-3	0-3	1-1	4-0	3-0	4-1	0-1	3-1	4-2	1-2		1-2	4-0	0-1	2-1	6-0	3-0
Northwich Victoria	1-0	2-1	3-0	4-2	1-1	0-1	0-1	3-0	1-0	0-1	4-0	1-6	4-3	2-3	1-0	1-1		0-1	4-1	0-1	2-0	3-1
Ossett Town	0-5	0-6	1-2	0-1	2-4	2-3	0-0	0-3	1-2	1-6	0-0	0-2	0-0	1-2	0-5	0-0	0-2		2-1	3-5	0-4	2-3
Retford United	1-2	0-0	0-2	1-3	0-4	3-5	0-2	0-4	1-3	2-5	2-1	0-3	0-4	0-2	3-2	1-2	0-1	0-2		0-0	0-3	0-3
Stocksbridge Park Steels	0-0	0-1	2-4	1-4	2-0	0-1	3-5	1-2	1-1	1-0	2-1	1-3	3-1	7-3	3-1	0-1	3-0	3-0	3-2		2-1	2-3
Whitby Town	2-1	1-2	2-2	1-0	0-1	2-2	1-5	0-1	2-2	1-0	2-2	1-1	1-2	3-2	3-1	1-0	2-4	3-1	2-1	2-0		0-3
Worksop Town	3-0	3-3	1-1	3-0	2-0	0-1	1-1	1-2	1-1	2-0	1-2	1-2	2-1	2-0	0-0	4-1	2-0	1-4	1-0	2-1	5-0	

Evo-Stik League Premier Division
Season 2010/2011

FC Halifax Town	42	30	8	4	108	36	98
Colwyn Bay	42	24	7	11	67	56	79
Bradford Park Avenue	42	23	8	11	84	55	77
FC United of Manchester	42	24	4	14	76	53	76
North Ferriby United	42	22	7	13	78	51	73
Buxton	42	20	10	12	71	52	70
Kendal Town	42	21	5	16	80	77	68
Marine	42	20	7	15	74	64	67
Worksop Town	42	21	6	15	72	54	66
Chasetown	42	20	6	16	76	59	66
Matlock Town	42	20	6	16	74	59	66
Northwich Victoria	42	18	9	15	66	55	63
Stocksbridge Park Steels	42	17	6	19	75	75	57
Ashton United	42	16	5	21	57	62	53
Mickleover Sports	42	15	7	20	70	76	52
Whitby Town	42	14	9	19	58	77	51
Nantwich Town	42	13	7	22	68	90	46
Frickley Athletic	42	11	11	20	43	68	44
Burscough	42	12	7	23	56	73	43
Hucknall Town	42	11	10	21	57	80	43

Ossett Town	42	9	5	28	45	103	32
Retford United	42	5	2	35	31	111	17

Worksop Town had 3 points deducted.

Burscough were reprieved from relegation due to Ilkeston Town folding in the Conference North earlier in the season.

Promotion Play-offs

Bradford Park Avenue 0   FC United of Manchester 2
Colwyn Bay 2   North Ferriby United 0

Colwyn Bay 1   FC United of Manchester 0

Promoted: FC Halifax Town and Colwyn Bay

Relegated: Hucknall Town, Ossett Town and Retford United

79

	Banbury United	Bashley	Bedford Town	Brackley Town	Cambridge City	Chesham United	Chippenham Town	Cirencester Town	Didcot Town	Evesham United	Halesowen Town	Hednesford Town	Hemel Hempstead Town	Leamington	Oxford City	Salisbury City	Stourbridge	Swindon Supermarine	Tiverton Town	Truro City	Weymouth
Banbury United		1-4	2-0	0-0	2-0	2-1	1-2	0-2	2-1	1-1	0-2	0-4	0-4	1-1	0-2	0-1	4-0	0-0	2-2	0-3	3-0
Bashley	2-1		2-5	0-3	1-1	1-1	1-4	1-2	1-1	1-0	0-0	0-4	1-0	0-4	3-1	0-2	0-0	2-0	1-0	2-1	5-1
Bedford Town	0-1	1-0		2-1	1-2	1-2	1-1	1-6	1-1	1-2	0-0	2-1	0-1	0-2	0-1	1-0	2-1	0-6	1-3	1-1	4-1
Brackley Town	2-0	3-4	4-0		0-0	1-1	1-1	4-1	2-1	5-0	6-0	0-0	3-1	0-0	1-0	0-3	0-0	1-4	1-0	3-2	1-1
Cambridge City	1-1	1-1	2-0	2-3		0-0	0-1	1-2	4-2	2-0	7-1	3-2	3-2	3-2	3-0	3-3	3-0	2-0	5-0	0-1	1-0
Chesham United	0-2	0-0	0-0	1-0	1-0		2-0	6-1	1-1	1-0	3-0	2-1	3-3	2-0	1-1	2-0	4-0	5-0	1-0	2-1	2-1
Chippenham Town	4-0	1-0	3-1	3-2	1-0	1-0		0-0	1-1	3-1	0-1	2-0	0-0	1-2	1-1	0-0	3-1	3-1	4-1	1-2	1-0
Cirencester Town	1-1	2-1	4-2	0-3	1-2	3-2	1-1		0-0	1-2	5-0	0-1	3-2	0-1	4-1	0-3	1-2	1-2	1-0	0-3	3-0
Didcot Town	0-2	0-2	1-0	1-1	1-2	1-0	1-1	1-2		1-2	1-1	0-3	0-1	1-2	0-3	1-1	1-4	2-0	2-0	0-3	2-2
Evesham United	4-3	2-2	0-0	1-0	1-2	0-0	2-2	2-1	3-0		0-0	4-1	1-0	0-1	3-0	0-0	2-3	0-1	3-1	3-4	1-3
Halesowen Town	3-1	0-2	0-3	5-3	0-1	1-4	1-2	1-1	1-0	0-8		0-6	1-6	0-3	0-3	0-4	0-3	1-1	0-1	0-3	0-0
Hednesford Town	1-0	1-0	4-1	2-0	0-2	3-2	0-2	3-1	1-1	1-0	4-2		2-0	1-1	2-1	3-0	2-3	1-1	2-0	1-0	9-0
Hemel Hempstead Town	1-2	0-2	1-0	1-0	0-2	0-1	1-2	2-2	0-1	1-0	1-0	0-1		1-0	0-2	0-3	2-2	1-2	1-1	1-1	1-2
Leamington	3-1	2-1	5-0	2-1	2-3	3-2	0-0	1-0	2-1	1-0	3-0	1-2	2-3		2-0	2-0	3-2	2-0	2-1	3-2	1-0
Oxford City	2-2	1-1	1-1	0-2	0-1	0-2	0-0	3-3	0-3	0-1	0-0	1-1	3-0	2-3		2-2	0-2	2-1	3-1	1-1	5-0
Salisbury City	4-1	2-1	4-1	3-1	1-3	3-2	4-0	4-1	4-2	0-3	7-1	2-1	1-1	0-0	2-0		3-0	2-0	3-0	0-6	3-2
Stourbridge	2-1	6-1	3-0	2-1	3-0	1-1	1-0	2-1	3-1	3-1	0-2	1-2	1-5	4-3	0-3	0-0		5-1	0-0	2-2	7-2
Swindon Supermarine	3-0	4-2	1-0	1-5	0-2	0-0	3-1	1-0	2-0	1-1	3-0	1-2	1-3	1-0	1-1	1-2	2-1		3-0	0-2	0-1
Tiverton Town	1-0	2-2	3-5	1-3	2-2	1-2	0-0	2-2	2-3	1-0	0-0	1-0	1-0	0-0	1-3	1-0	0-1	1-2		1-2	0-4
Truro City	1-0	2-1	0-1	1-0	2-0	0-3	5-0	0-2	2-1	1-1	6-0	1-0	3-0	3-1	2-1	1-1	3-1	7-2	3-0		3-2
Weymouth	2-4	1-4	3-1	0-0	0-3	3-0	3-3	1-0	1-2	2-0	3-0	2-4	2-2	1-2	1-1	2-0	3-2	0-0	3-1	0-4	

Southern League Premier Division

Season 2010/2011

Truro City	40	27	6	7	91	35	87
Hednesford Town	40	26	5	9	82	38	83
Salisbury City	40	23	10	7	82	45	79
Cambridge City	40	24	7	9	74	40	79
Leamington	40	24	6	10	68	39	78
Chesham United	40	20	11	9	64	35	71
Chippenham Town	40	18	14	8	54	41	68
Stourbridge	40	18	8	14	72	61	62
Brackley Town	40	16	10	14	67	47	58
Swindon Supermarine	40	17	7	16	56	58	58
Bashley	40	14	10	16	55	63	52
Evesham United	40	14	9	17	54	49	51
Cirencester Town	40	13	8	19	59	67	47
Oxford City	40	11	12	17	48	54	45
Hemel Hempstead Town	40	13	6	21	50	54	45
Banbury United	40	11	8	21	44	67	40
Bedford Town	40	10	7	23	41	76	37
Weymouth	40	12	8	20	55	85	34
Didcot Town	40	7	11	22	39	69	32
Tiverton Town	40	7	8	25	33	77	29
Halesowen Town	40	5	9	26	24	107	24

Weymouth had 10 points deducted.
Banbury United had 1 point deducted.
Windsor & Eton was wound up in the High Court on 2nd February 2011, due to unpaid taxes. The club's record was expunged on 8th February 2011:   26   8   12   6   33   35   36

Promotion Play-offs

Hednesford Town 3   Leamington 1
Salisbury City 1   Cambridge City 0

Hednesford Town 2   Salisbury City .... 2 (aet.)
Salisbury City won 3-2 on penalties

Promoted: Truro City and Salisbury City

Relegated: Didcot Town, Tiverton Town and Halesowen Town

Ryman League Premier Division 2010/2011 Season

	AFC Hornchurch	Aveley	Billericay Town	Bury Town	Canvey Island	Carshalton Athletic	Concord Rangers	Cray Wanderers	Croydon Athletic	Folkestone Invicta	Harrow Borough	Hastings United	Hendon	Horsham	Kingstonian	Lowestoft Town	Maidstone United	Margate	Sutton United	Tonbridge Angels	Tooting & Mitcham United	Wealdstone
AFC Hornchurch		1-0	1-1	1-1	0-3	4-0	2-0	1-0	1-0	4-0	2-0	1-0	0-0	0-2	1-1	1-2	2-0	2-1	1-1	3-1	2-2	2-2
Aveley	1-4		0-1	0-2	1-3	2-0	1-1	0-3	3-0	1-1	0-2	1-3	0-2	1-0	1-1	0-3	1-2	1-1	0-0	0-3	3-1	0-1
Billericay Town	2-0	1-0		1-2	1-0	0-0	2-1	3-2	1-2	4-2	1-3	3-0	2-0	2-1	0-1	1-3	1-0	0-0	1-0	3-0	1-0	1-0
Bury Town	1-3	2-1	3-0		2-1	3-0	1-2	2-2	1-0	1-1	2-5	2-1	2-2	2-0	0-0	0-0	1-2	2-1	2-1	1-2	2-1	1-0
Canvey Island	3-0	2-1	3-2	3-0		1-1	0-4	4-2	3-2	1-0	2-0	2-2	4-1	3-1	0-2	0-0	3-0	2-0	1-3	1-0	0-2	1-1
Carshalton Athletic	0-0	2-2	1-3	1-0	1-0		2-4	1-1	1-2	1-0	0-1	1-1	2-1	0-0	1-3	2-0	0-0	1-3	0-2	3-2	2-0	2-3
Concord Rangers	1-3	0-1	1-1	2-2	1-0	1-1		2-0	3-0	2-1	3-0	2-1	3-2	2-0	2-1	0-2	3-2	0-0	0-0	1-2	3-0	1-6
Cray Wanderers	1-2	3-0	1-3	2-1	0-0	2-1	2-1		4-0	0-1	5-1	2-0	3-1	1-1	2-0	0-1	2-1	2-0	0-2	0-1	2-3	1-0
Croydon Athletic	0-3	0-2	0-0	1-3	0-4	1-4	1-3	3-1		2-1	1-3	2-0	1-4	2-4	0-4	0-2	1-2	5-3	0-3	2-0	0-1	2-2
Folkestone Invicta	1-1	1-2	1-1	0-2	1-2	1-2	1-1	1-1	0-2		1-0	1-3	1-2	0-0	1-0	1-4	4-0	1-2	0-2	0-0	1-3	1-1
Harrow Borough	1-0	1-2	1-1	2-0	6-1	2-1	0-2	1-1	3-1	2-0		2-2	2-3	6-0	1-0	2-0	2-0	0-0	0-0	2-0	2-0	2-4
Hastings United	0-1	2-3	1-0	0-2	0-1	0-1	0-3	1-1	3-1	2-2	2-0		1-1	2-3	1-2	0-0	1-0	3-0	2-3	1-2	3-2	2-0
Hendon	2-1	1-2	1-1	3-3	0-3	1-0	4-1	2-2	4-0	2-1	0-3	0-0		4-0	2-3	1-1	2-3	2-3	1-0	0-3	4-1	0-1
Horsham	0-0	0-0	1-2	1-4	1-1	2-1	1-3	0-4	1-1	0-0	1-7	1-1	1-2		2-3	1-2	1-1	1-1	3-1	0-2	1-0	2-1
Kingstonian	2-1	2-0	4-2	1-1	3-1	0-1	0-3	2-1	2-1	0-1	1-3	3-1	3-0	1-3		2-0	0-1	1-0	1-0	1-1	4-2	1-3
Lowestoft Town	2-0	1-0	1-1	0-1	1-1	0-0	2-0	0-1	4-0	4-1	3-0	1-1	8-1	4-0	1-1		3-3	2-1	0-0	0-0	0-0	0-0
Maidstone United	0-0	1-1	0-2	1-2	0-1	1-3	2-0	2-4	0-1	2-0	0-0	2-4	2-2	0-1	1-2	0-1		0-2	0-1	0-3	1-1	2-4
Margate	2-2	2-0	0-1	0-1	2-2	2-1	1-2	0-2	0-2	0-2	2-3	2-0	1-1	6-1	3-3	0-3	1-1		3-2	0-1	3-3	1-0
Sutton United	3-0	2-1	1-0	2-1	2-0	2-0	1-1	1-1	5-0	2-1	2-1	3-0	2-0	2-0	2-1	5-1	2-1	5-1		2-2	2-2	4-3
Tonbridge Angels	7-1	1-0	3-1	2-3	1-1	4-0	3-2	0-4	1-0	1-0	1-2	2-0	2-1	2-0	1-1	3-3	1-0	1-1	0-1		3-3	2-0
Tooting & Mitcham United	1-1	1-2	3-2	1-3	1-2	0-5	3-2	0-3	2-2	4-1	3-2	1-1	4-3	2-2	1-1	2-1	3-4	3-0	0-3	1-5		1-0
Wealdstone	0-3	2-0	1-0	0-0	3-3	0-3	1-3	0-1	4-3	1-1	1-1	2-1	1-0	3-0	2-1	0-2	1-1	0-1	2-1	0-0	3-0	

Ryman League Premier Division

Season 2010/2011

Team	P	W	D	L	F	A	Pts
Sutton United	42	26	9	7	76	33	87
Tonbridge Angels	42	22	10	10	71	45	76
Bury Town	42	22	10	10	67	49	76
Lowestoft Town	42	20	15	7	68	30	75
Harrow Borough	42	22	7	13	77	51	73
Canvey Island	42	21	10	11	69	51	73
Kingstonian	42	21	9	12	66	50	72
Concord Rangers	42	21	8	13	72	55	71
Cray Wanderers	42	20	9	13	72	46	69
AFC Hornchurch	42	19	12	11	60	46	69
Billericay Town	42	20	9	13	56	45	69
Wealdstone	42	16	10	16	58	54	58
Carshalton Athletic	42	14	10	18	49	57	52
Tooting & Mitcham United	42	13	10	19	63	85	49
Hendon	42	12	10	20	61	81	46
Margate	42	11	12	19	52	64	45
Horsham	42	11	11	20	43	77	44
Hastings United	42	9	11	22	50	65	38
Aveley	42	10	8	24	35	62	38
Maidstone United	42	9	10	23	43	75	37
Croydon Athletic	42	10	4	28	44	95	31
Folkestone Invicta	42	5	12	25	34	68	27

Croydon Athletic had 3 points deducted.

Promotion Play-offs

Bury Town 1   Lowestoft Town 2
Tonbridge Angels 3   Harrow Borough .... 2 (aet.)

Tonbridge Angels 4   Lowestoft Town 3

Promoted: Sutton United and Tonbridge Angels

Relegated: Aveley, Maidstone United, Croydon Athletic and Folkestone Invicta

F.A. Trophy 2010/2011

Qualifying 1	AFC Hornchurch	2	Brentwood Town	1
Qualifying 1	AFC Totton	5	AFC Hayes	0
Qualifying 1	Almondsbury Town	1	Didcot Town	0
Qualifying 1	Arlesey Town	0	Ramsgate	0
Qualifying 1	Ashford Town (Middlesex)	6	North Greenford United	2
Qualifying 1	Banbury United	1	Wimborne Town	1
Qualifying 1	Bideford	4	Tiverton Town	2
Qualifying 1	Biggleswade Town	0	Billericay Town	1
Qualifying 1	Bognor Regis Town	1	Croydon Athletic	0
Qualifying 1	Bridgwater Town	1	Stourbridge	3
Qualifying 1	Burnham	0	Brackley Town	0
Qualifying 1	Burscough	0	Clitheroe	2
Qualifying 1	Bury Town	2	Barton Rovers	0
Qualifying 1	Buxton	1	Stocksbridge Park Steels	2
Qualifying 1	Cambridge City	1	Aveley	0
Qualifying 1	Cammell Laird	1	Witton Albion	2
Qualifying 1	Canvey Island	1	AFC Sudbury	2
Qualifying 1	Carlton Town	1	Rushall Olympic	1
Qualifying 1	Carshalton Athletic	2	Ilford	0
Qualifying 1	Chesham United	1	Salisbury City	1
Qualifying 1	Chorley	1	Quorn	0
Qualifying 1	Cinderford Town	2	Hungerford Town	2
Qualifying 1	Cirencester Town	3	Halesowen Town	0
Qualifying 1	Colwyn Bay	2	Bradford Park Avenue	0
Qualifying 1	Cray Wanderers	2	Wingate & Finchley	1
Qualifying 1	Curzon Ashton	3	Skelmersdale United	1
Qualifying 1	Dulwich Hamlet	2	Hastings United	2
Qualifying 1	Durham City	0	FC Halifax Town	2
Qualifying 1	Enfield Town	2	Walton Casuals	1
Qualifying 1	Evesham United	1	Frome Town	0
Qualifying 1	FC United of Manchester	5	Newcastle Town	0
Qualifying 1	Faversham Town	1	Kingstonian	2
Qualifying 1	Fleet Town	0	Godalming Town	2
Qualifying 1	Folkestone Invicta	4	Worthing	2
Qualifying 1	Glapwell	2	Stamford	0
Qualifying 1	Great Wakering Rovers	1	Thamesmead Town	2
Qualifying 1	Harlow Town	3	Bedford Town	2
Qualifying 1	Harrogate Railway Athletic	2	Ossett Albion	1
Qualifying 1	Harrow Borough	0	Hendon	1
Qualifying 1	Hednesford Town	1	Whitby Town	2
Qualifying 1	Hemel Hempstead Town	2	Rugby Town	3
Qualifying 1	Horsham	3	Redbridge	0
Qualifying 1	Kendal Town	3	Frickley Athletic	0
Qualifying 1	Lancaster City	4	Ossett Town	2
Qualifying 1	Maidstone United	2	Burgess Hill Town	0
Qualifying 1	Margate	5	Whitehawk	1
Qualifying 1	Marine	2	Ashton United	2
Qualifying 1	Matlock Town	10	Bedworth United	0
Qualifying 1	Mickleover Sports	2	Hucknall Town	1
Qualifying 1	Market Drayton Town	1	Worksop Town	1
Qualifying 1	North Ferriby United	0	Bamber Bridge	2
Qualifying 1	Nantwich Town	6	Prescot Cables	2
Qualifying 1	Needham Market	2	Lowestoft Town	2
Qualifying 1	Northwich Victoria	0	Lincoln United	0

Qualifying 1	Oxford City	1	Daventry Town	4	
Qualifying 1	Paulton Rovers	3	North Leigh	3	
Qualifying 1	Radcliffe Borough	1	Garforth Town	1	
Qualifying 1	Retford United	2	Romulus	2	
Qualifying 1	Sheffield	1	Chasetown	1	
Qualifying 1	Shepshed Dynamo	1	Mossley	4	
Qualifying 1	Slough Town	1	Chippenham Town	1	
Qualifying 1	Soham Town Rangers	1	Grays Athletic	2	
Qualifying 1	Sutton United	3	Tooting & Mitcham United	1	
Qualifying 1	Swindon Supermarine	4	Beaconsfield SYCOB	2	
Qualifying 1	Tonbridge Angels	3	Concord Rangers	2	
Qualifying 1	Truro City	1	Bishop's Cleeve	0	
Qualifying 1	Uxbridge	4	Abingdon United	1	
Qualifying 1	Waltham Forest	0	Romford	2	
Qualifying 1	Wealdstone	2	Potters Bar Town	2	
Qualifying 1	Weymouth	2	Bashley	1	
Qualifying 1	Windsor & Eton	1	Aylesbury	1	
Qualifying 1	Woodford United	1	Leamington	3	
Replay	Ashton United	1	Marine	3	
Replay	Aylesbury	1	Windsor & Eton	2	
Replay	Brackley Town	4	Burnham	0	
Replay	Chasetown	3	Sheffield	1	
Replay	Chippenham Town	4	Slough Town	1	
Replay	Garforth Town	1	Radcliffe Borough	2	
Replay	Hastings United	1	Dulwich Hamlet	2	
Replay	Hungerford Town	1	Cinderford Town	2	(aet)
Replay	Lincoln United	2	Northwich Victoria	3	
Replay	Lowestoft Town	6	Needham Market	2	
Replay	North Leigh	1	Paulton Rovers	2	
Replay	Potters Bar Town	1	Wealdstone	3	
Replay	Ramsgate	2	Arlesey Town	3	(aet)
Replay	Romulus	2	Retford United	1	
Replay	Rushall Olympic	4	Carlton Town	1	
Replay	Salisbury City	2	Chesham United	1	
Replay	Wimborne Town	1	Banbury United	3	(aet)
Replay	Worksop Town	1	Market Drayton Town	0	
Qualifying 2	AFC Sudbury	5	Hendon	1	
Qualifying 2	AFC Totton	1	Romford	3	
Qualifying 2	Arlesey Town	2	Uxbridge	2	
Qualifying 2	Ashford Town (Middlesex)	2	Bury Town	1	
Qualifying 2	Bideford	1	Dulwich Hamlet	0	
Qualifying 2	Billericay Town	2	Banbury United	1	
Qualifying 2	Bognor Regis Town	1	Godalming Town	1	
Qualifying 2	Brackley Town	4	Windsor & Eton	0	
Qualifying 2	Chippenham Town	1	Lowestoft Town	1	
Qualifying 2	Chorley	3	Marine	1	
Qualifying 2	Cirencester Town	2	Weymouth	1	
Qualifying 2	Cray Wanderers	1	Maidstone United	2	
Qualifying 2	Curzon Ashton	2	FC Halifax Town	1	
Qualifying 2	Daventry Town	1	Cambridge City	2	
Qualifying 2	Evesham United	0	Sutton United	1	
Qualifying 2	FC United of Manchester	2	Colwyn Bay	1	
Qualifying 2	Folkestone Invicta	0	Thamesmead Town	0	
Qualifying 2	Grays Athletic	2	Cinderford Town	1	
Qualifying 2	Harlow Town	2	Carshalton Athletic	0	
Qualifying 2	Kendal Town	1	Matlock Town	1	

Qualifying 2	Kingstonian	3	Wealdstone	5	
Qualifying 2	Leamington	3	Bamber Bridge	0	
Qualifying 2	Lowestoft Town	3	Chippenham Town	1	(aet)
Qualifying 2	Margate	1	AFC Hornchurch	2	
Qualifying 2	Mickleover Sports	2	Chasetown	5	
Qualifying 2	Mossley	2	Nantwich Town	3	
Qualifying 2	Northwich Victoria	4	Glapwell	0	
Qualifying 2	Paulton Rovers	4	Swindon Supermarine	5	
Qualifying 2	Radcliffe Borough	1	Witton Albion	1	
Qualifying 2	Romulus	1	Harrogate Railway Athletic	2	
Qualifying 2	Rushall Olympic	0	Stourbridge	1	
Qualifying 2	Salisbury City	2	Almondsbury Town	1	
Qualifying 2	Stocksbridge Park Steels	3	Rugby Town	2	
Qualifying 2	Tonbridge Angels	2	Enfield Town	0	
Qualifying 2	Truro City	2	Horsham	0	
Qualifying 2	Whitby Town	3	Clitheroe	1	
Qualifying 2	Worksop Town	2	Lancaster City	1	
Replay	Godalming Town	2	Bognor Regis Town	5	
Replay	Matlock Town	1	Kendal Town	2	
Replay	Thamesmead Town	1	Folkestone Invicta	3	
Replay	Uxbridge	4	Arlesey Town	2	
Replay	Witton Albion	3	Radcliffe Borough	1	
Qualifying 3	AFC Telford United	2	Corby Town	1	
Qualifying 3	Alfreton Town	4	Kendal Town	0	
Qualifying 3	Basingstoke Town	2	Havant & Waterlooville	2	
Qualifying 3	Bideford	0	AFC Hornchurch	3	
Qualifying 3	Blyth Spartans	1	Stafford Rangers	0	
Qualifying 3	Bognor Regis Town	2	Hampton & Richmond Borough	2	
Qualifying 3	Boreham Wood	3	Romford	0	
Qualifying 3	Boston United	2	Gainsborough Trinity	1	
Qualifying 3	Brackley Town	0	Wealdstone	1	
Qualifying 3	Braintree Town	2	Farnborough	0	
Qualifying 3	Bishop's Stortford	1	Ashford Town (Middlesex)	2	
Qualifying 3	Chorley	0	Guiseley	1	
Qualifying 3	Cirencester Town	2	Grays Athletic	2	
Qualifying 3	Curzon Ashton	2	Solihull Moors	1	
Qualifying 3	Dover Athletic	1	Woking	2	
Qualifying 3	Droylsden	3	Stourbridge	2	
Qualifying 3	Eastleigh	2	Folkestone Invicta	1	
Qualifying 3	Eastwood Town	2	Cambridge City	0	
Qualifying 3	Ebbsfleet United	4	Bromley	0	
Qualifying 3	FC United of Manchester	1	Hinckley United	2	
Qualifying 3	Harlow Town	3	Maidstone United	0	
Qualifying 3	Harrogate Railway Athletic	3	Nantwich Town	4	
Qualifying 3	Harrogate Town	1	Witton Albion	1	
Qualifying 3	Leamington	1	Hyde	2	
Qualifying 3	Lewes	1	Salisbury City	3	
Qualifying 3	Lowestoft Town	2	Swindon Supermarine	1	
Qualifying 3	Maidenhead United	2	Uxbridge	4	
Qualifying 3	Nuneaton Town	1	Worcester City	2	
Qualifying 3	Redditch United	80	Bye	0	
Qualifying 3	St. Albans City	3	Staines Town	1	
Qualifying 3	Sutton United	4	Billericay Town	2	
Qualifying 3	Thurrock	0	Dartford	2	
Qualifying 3	Truro City	1	AFC Sudbury	2	
Qualifying 3	Vauxhall Motors (Cheshire)	1	Stalybridge Celtic	3	

Qualifying 3	Welling United	1	Tonbridge Angels	0	
Qualifying 3	Weston-Super-Mare	1	Dorchester Town	3	
Qualifying 3	Whitby Town	2	Northwich Victoria	2	
Qualifying 3	Workington	0	Chasetown	0	
Qualifying 3	Worksop Town	1	Chelmsford City	0	
Qualifying 3	Worksop Town	4	Stocksbridge Park Steels	1	
Replay	Chasetown	4	Workington	0	
Replay	Grays Athletic	0	Cirencester Town	1	
Replay	Hampton & Richmond Borough	2	Bognor Regis Town	0	
Replay	Havant & Waterlooville	1	Basingstoke Town	2	
Replay	Northwich Victoria	1	Whitby Town	0	
Replay	Witton Albion	1	Harrogate Town	2	
Round 1	AFC Sudbury	1	Hampton & Richmond Borough	4	
Round 1	AFC Wimbledon	3	Braintree Town	0	
Round 1	Alfreton Town	3	Hyde	0	
Round 1	Ashford Town (Middlesex)	1	AFC Hornchurch	0	
Round 1	Barrow	2	Guiseley	3	
Round 1	Basingstoke Town	0	Salisbury City	2	
Round 1	Blyth Spartans	2	Fleetwood Town	0	
Round 1	Cambridge United	2	Forest Green Rovers	1	
Round 1	Chasetown	3	Kettering Town	3	
Round 1	Cirencester Town	1	Gloucester City	1	
Round 1	Crawley Town	3	Dartford	3	
Round 1	Curzon Ashton	2	Altrincham	1	
	The match was abandoned at half-time due to power failure and a replay was ordered.				
Round 1	Darlington	3	Tamworth	2	
Round 1	Dorchester Town	3	St. Albans City	0	
Round 1	Droylsden	4	Hinckley United	3	
Round 1	Eastbourne Borough	3	Boreham Wood	1	
Round 1	Eastleigh	1	Sutton United	1	
Round 1	Ebbsfleet United	3	Hayes & Yeading United	1	
Round 1	Gateshead	2	Southport	2	
Round 1	Grimsby Town	3	Redditch United	0	
Round 1	Harlow Town	0	Woking	2	
Round 1	Harrogate Town	0	AFC Telford United	3	
Round 1	Histon	2	Bath City	3	
Round 1	Lowestoft Town	2	Uxbridge	3	
Round 1	Luton Town	0	Welling United	0	
Round 1	Newport County	0	Wealdstone	0	
Round 1	Rushden & Diamonds	1	Eastwood Town	1	
Round 1	Stalybridge Celtic	2	Nantwich Town	1	
Round 1	Worcester City	1	Northwich Victoria	0	
Round 1	Worksop Town	0	Mansfield Town	5	
	Match played at Retford				
Round 1	Wrexham	2	Kidderminster Harriers	0	
Round 1	York City	0	Boston United	1	
Replay	Curzon Ashton	0	Altrincham	2	
Replay	Dartford	1	Crawley Town	0	
Replay	Eastwood Town	4	Rushden & Diamonds	3	(aet)
Replay	Gloucester City	3	Cirencester Town	0	
Replay	Kettering Town	1	Chasetown	2	(aet)
Replay	Southport	0	Gateshead	1	
Replay	Sutton United	0	Eastleigh	4	
Replay	Wealdstone	0	Newport County	1	(aet)
Replay	Welling United	1	Luton Town	2	

Round 2	AFC Telford United	1	Eastwood Town	0	
Round 2	AFC Wimbledon	2	Woking	3	
Round 2	Alfreton Town	3	Cambridge United	3	
Round 2	Ashford Town (Middlesex)	0	Dartford	1	
Round 2	Blyth Spartans	2	Altrincham	1	
Round 2	Boston United	0	Gloucester City	1	
Round 2	Chasetown	2	Grimsby Town	1	
Round 2	Darlington	4	Bath City	1	
Round 2	Dorchester Town	3	Eastbourne Borough	3	
Round 2	Droylsden	1	Ebbsfleet United	0	
Round 2	Eastleigh	3	Worcester City	3	
Round 2	Gateshead	6	Hampton & Richmond Borough	0	
Round 2	Guiseley	2	Stalybridge Celtic	1	
Round 2	Luton Town	4	Uxbridge	0	
Round 2	Mansfield Town	4	Newport County	2	
Round 2	Salisbury City	1	Wrexham	0	
Replay	Cambridge United	3	Alfreton Town	6	(aet)
Replay	Eastbourne Borough	1	Dorchester Town	0	
Replay	Worcester City	1	Eastleigh	4	
Round 3	AFC Telford United	0	Darlington	3	
Round 3	Blyth Spartans	2	Droylsden	2	
Round 3	Eastbourne Borough	1	Guiseley	1	
Round 3	Eastleigh	1	Chasetown	3	
Round 3	Gateshead	3	Dartford	0	
Round 3	Luton Town	1	Gloucester City	0	
Round 3	Mansfield Town	1	Alfreton Town	1	
Round 3	Woking	0	Salisbury City	2	
Replay	Alfreton Town	1	Mansfield Town	2	
Replay	Droylsden	0	Blyth Spartans	4	
Replay	Guiseley	2	Eastbourne Borough	1	
Round 4	Blyth Spartans	0	Gateshead	2	
Round 4	Chasetown	2	Mansfield Town	2	
Round 4	Darlington	2	Salisbury City	1	
Round 4	Guiseley	0	Luton Town	1	
Replay	Mansfield Town	3	Chasetown	1	
Semi-finals					
1st leg	Darlington	3	Gateshead	2	
2nd leg	Gateshead	0	Darlington	0	
	Darlington won 3-2 on aggregate.				
1st leg	Mansfield Town	1	Luton Town	0	
2nd leg	Luton Town	1	Mansfield Town	1	(aet)
	Mansfield Town won 2-1 on aggregate				
FINAL	Darlington	1	Mansfield Town	0	

F.A. Vase 2010/2011

Round 1	AFC Dunstable	3	Colney Heath	1	
Round 1	AFC Emley	3	Runcorn Linnets	1	
Round 1	AFC Liverpool	3	Hallam	0	
Round 1	Atherton Laburnum Rovers	2	Runcorn Town	3	
Round 1	Aylesbury United	4	Hertford Town	3	(aet)
Round 1	Baldock Town Letchworth	0	Holyport	1	
Round 1	Barking	1	Flackwell Heath	2	
Round 1	Bedlington Terriers	0	Spennymoor Town	1	
Round 1	Bemerton Heath Harlequins	5	Lydney Town	2	(aet)
Round 1	Billingham Town	3	Ashington	4	(aet)
Round 1	Binfield	3	Hillingdon Borough	2	
Round 1	Bishop Auckland	3	Billingham Synthonia	4	(aet)
Round 1	Bishop Sutton	2	Keynsham Town	2	(aet)
Round 1	Blaby & Whetstone Athletic	2	Westfields	5	
Round 1	Bloxwich United	5	Pilkington XXX	0	
Round 1	Boldmere St. Michaels	1	Continental Star	0	
Round 1	Bookham	0	Herne Bay	4	
Round 1	Bracknell Town	2	Wodson Park	0	
Round 1	Brading Town	4	St. Francis Rangers	2	
Round 1	Brighouse Town	3	Eccleshill United	3	(aet)
Round 1	Brislington	0	St. Blazey	1	
Round 1	Burnham Ramblers	2	Kentish Town	0	(aet)
Round 1	Cadbury Heath	2	Wootton Bassett Town	1	
Round 1	Calne Town	1	Downton	2	
Round 1	Camberley Town	2	Blackfield & Langley	1	
Round 1	Cambridge Regional College	4	Wellingborough Town	0	
Round 1	Chalfont St. Peter	6	Newbury (2)	0	
Round 1	Clanfield 85	2	Fairford Town	1	
Round 1	Coalville Town	2	Stratford Town	1	
Round 1	Cockfosters	0	Witham Town	3	
Round 1	Colliers Wood United	5	Cove	2	
Round 1	Corinthian	0	Tunbridge Wells	4	
Round 1	Coventry Copsewood	2	Heath Town Rangers	1	
Round 1	Coventry Sphinx	4	Anstey Nomads	3	
Round 1	Crawley Down	0	Rye United	1	
Round 1	Croydon	3	Beckenham Town	7	
Round 1	Dunkirk	2	Blidworth Welfare	0	
Round 1	Dunstable Town	5	AFC Wallingford	0	
Round 1	Dunston UTS	2	Washington	1	
Round 1	Eccleshall	2	Bridgnorth Town	4	
Round 1	Egham Town	2	Molesey	0	
Round 1	Erith & Belvedere	2	Chichester City	1	(aet)
Round 1	Eton Manor	4	FC Clacton	2	
Round 1	Fisher	1	Warlingham	3	
Round 1	Forest Town	3	Greenwood Meadows	1	
Round 1	Formby	2	Flixton	0	
Round 1	Gedling Town	2	Glossop North End	1	
Round 1	Godmanchester Rovers	4	Framlingham Town	0	
Round 1	Gorleston	1	Hadleigh United	0	
Round 1	Guildford City (2)	3	Horley Town	2	(aet)
Round 1	Haringey Borough	1	Tring Athletic	3	
Round 1	Heanor Town	6	Clipstone Welfare	2	
Round 1	Holbrook Sports	4	Arnold Town	4	(aet)
Round 1	Holwell Sports	4	Tividale	3	
Round 1	Ilfracombe Town	1	Hengrove Athletic	2	

Round 1	Ipswich Wanderers	1	Walsham Le Willows	2	
Round 1	Irlam	2	Colne	0	
Round 1	Kidlington	0	Bitton	1	
Round 1	Lancing	1	Christchurch	1	(aet)
Round 1	Langford	1	Hullbridge Sports	3	
Round 1	Leeds Carnegie	4	Easington Colliery	0	
Round 1	Leiston	3	Haverhill Rovers	2	(aet)
Round 1	Leverstock Green	5	Enfield 1893	4	
Round 1	Lordswood	1	Three Bridges	2	
Round 1	Louth Town	3	Barton Town Old Boys	3	
Round 1	Lymington Town	1	Bournemouth (Ams)	2	
Round 1	Maine Road	2	AFC Blackpool	2	(aet)
Round 1	Malvern Town	2	Heather St. Johns	6	
Round 1	Melksham Town	3	Laverstock & Ford	1	
Round 1	Moneyfields	1	Greenwich Borough	0	
Round 1	Newport (IOW)	3	Shoreham	0	
Round 1	Northallerton Town	3	Stokesley	4	
Round 1	Odd Down	7	Bridport	0	
Round 1	Peacehaven & Telscombe	1	Hamble ASSC	0	
Round 1	Ramsbottom United	0	Staveley Miners Welfare	1	
Round 1	Raynes Park Vale	0	Hythe Town	3	
Round 1	Reading Town	4	Newport Pagnell Town	2	
Round 1	Rossendale United	0	Bacup Borough	2	
Round 1	Saltash United	9	Newquay	1	
Round 1	Scarborough Athletic	2	Bridlington Town	2	(aet)
Round 1	Sherborne Town	2	Bodmin Town	2	(aet)
Round 1	South Shields	0	Thackley	2	
Round 1	St. Helens Town	2	Oldham Boro	1	
	Match played at Ashton Town FC				
Round 1	St. Neots Town	11	Felixstowe & Walton United	0	
Round 1	Stansted	2	Takeley	0	
Round 1	Stanway Rovers	4	London APSA	0	
Round 1	Stone Dominoes	1	Heath Hayes	4	
Round 1	Tadcaster Albion	2	Tow Law Town	0	
Round 1	Thrapston Town	2	King's Lynn Town	4	
Round 1	Thurnby Nirvana	1	Shifnal Town	2	
Round 1	Torpoint Athletic	4	Radstock Town	1	
Round 1	Verwood Town	1	Budleigh Salterton	0	(aet)
Round 1	Wantage Town	2	Shrivenham	1	
Round 1	Wednesfield	4	Studley	3	
Round 1	Wellington	5	Tavistock	0	
Round 1	West Auckland Town	6	Birtley Town	0	
Round 1	Whitton United	2	Norwich United	0	
Round 1	Wick	0	VCD Athletic	2	(aet)
Round 1	Willenhall Town	0	Gornal Athletic	2	
Round 1	Winterton Rangers	3	Deeping Rangers	1	
Round 1	Wisbech Town	5	Cogenhoe United	1	
Round 1	Wolverhampton Casuals	1	Bustleholme	3	
Replay	AFC Blackpool	2	Maine Road	1	
Replay	Arnold Town	1	Holbrook Sports	3	
Replay	Barton Town Old Boys	1	Louth Town	0	(aet)
Replay	Bodmin Town	1	Sherborne Town	0	
Replay	Bridlington Town	1	Scarborough Athletic	3	
Replay	Christchurch	0	Lancing	1	
Replay	Eccleshill United	2	Brighouse Town	1	
Replay	Keynsham Town	1	Bishop Sutton	0	

Round 2	AFC Blackpool	0	AFC Liverpool	2	
Round 2	AFC Dunstable	1	Tring Athletic	2	
Round 2	Beckenham Town	2	Peacehaven & Telscombe	1	(aet)
Round 2	Billingham Synthonia	3	Stokesley	1	
Round 2	Bitton	2	Shortwood United	1	
Round 2	Boldmere St. Michaels	1	Gornal Athletic	2	
Round 2	Bootle	1	Shildon	3	
Round 2	Bournemouth (Ams)	5	Odd Down	0	
Round 2	Bridgnorth Town	2	Coalville Town	4	
Round 2	Bristol Manor Farm	3	Torpoint Athletic	7	
Round 2	Bustleholme	2	Barton Town Old Boys	0	
Round 2	Causeway United	2	Gedling Town	0	
Round 2	Chertsey Town	1	Moneyfields	2	
Round 2	Clanfield 85	0	Bemerton Heath Harlequins	3	
Round 2	Colliers Wood United	1	Witney United	0	
	Played at Croydon FC				
Round 2	Coventry Sphinx	0	Dunkirk	3	
Round 2	Dawlish Town	0	Bodmin Town	2	
Round 2	Downton	2	Cadbury Heath	3	
Round 2	Dunstable Town	2	Cambridge Regional College	1	
Round 2	Dunston UTS	4	AFC Emley	0	
Round 2	Eccleshill United	0	Runcorn Town	2	
Round 2	Egham Town	1	Newport (IOW)	2	
Round 2	Epsom & Ewell	4	Bracknell Town	0	
Round 2	Erith & Belvedere	0	Lancing	2	
Round 2	Flackwell Heath	1	Three Bridges	2	
Round 2	Forest Town	0	Tadcaster Albion	4	
Round 2	Formby	1	Bacup Borough	0	
Round 2	Godmanchester Rovers	0	Stanway Rovers	1	
Round 2	Gresley	2	Heanor Town	0	
Round 2	Guildford City	5	Brading Town	2	
Round 2	Heath Hayes	2	Tipton Town	1	
Round 2	Herne Bay	3	Camberley Town	0	
Round 2	Holbrook Sports	7	Holwell Sports	0	
Round 2	Hullbridge Sports	1	Leverstock Green	5	
Round 2	King's Lynn Town	4	Gorleston	0	
Round 2	Kirkley & Pakefield	0	Long Buckby	1	
Round 2	Leeds Carnegie	4	Marske United	3	(aet)
Round 2	New Mills	2	Ashington	4	
Round 2	Norton & Stockton Ancients	4	Irlam	3	
Round 2	Plymouth Parkway	6	Melksham Town	1	
Round 2	Poole Town	4	Wellington	3	
Round 2	Reading Town	1	Warlingham	0	
Round 2	Royston Town	2	Leiston	2	(aet)
Round 2	Rye United	4	Chalfont St. Peter	4	(aet)
	Match played at Sussex County Ground, Lancing				
Round 2	Scarborough Athletic	2	Armthorpe Welfare	2	(aet)
Round 2	Shifnal Town	2	Bloxwich United	2	(aet)
Round 2	St. Blazey	1	Hengrove Athletic	1	(aet)
Round 2	St. Ives Town	2	Aylesbury United	1	
Round 2	St. Neots Town	6	Burnham Ramblers	1	
Round 2	Stansted	3	Eton Manor	1	
Round 2	Staveley Miners Welfare	1	Pickering Town	0	(aet)
Round 2	Stotfold	2	Whitton United	1	
Round 2	Thackley	0	Whitley Bay	1	
Round 2	Tunbridge Wells	8	Holyport	0	
Round 2	VCD Athletic	1	Hythe Town	5	

Round 2	Verwood Town	2	Keynsham Town	1	
Round 2	Wantage Town	3	Binfield	1	
Round 2	Wednesfield	1	Heather St. Johns	3	(aet)
Round 2	West Auckland Town	1	Spennymoor Town	3	
Round 2	Westfields	3	Coventry Copsewood	0	
Round 2	Willand Rovers	2	Saltash United	1	
Round 2	Winterton Rangers	0	St. Helens Town	2	
Round 2	Witham Town	3	Walsham Le Willows	1	
Round 2	Wroxham	4	Wisbech Town	0	
Replay	Armthorpe Welfare	2	Scarborough Athletic	3	
Replay	Bloxwich United	5	Shifnal Town	3	
Replay	Chalfont St. Peter	1	Rye United	2	
Replay	Hengrove Athletic	0	St. Blazey	2	
Replay	Leiston	1	Royston Town	0	
Round 3	Beckenham Town	1	King's Lynn Town	2	
Round 3	Bitton	4	Newport (IOW)	1	
Round 3	Cadbury Heath	4	Reading Town	1	
Round 3	Causeway United	0	Norton & Stockton Ancients	3	
Round 3	Dunkirk	1	Ashington	2	
Round 3	Dunston UTS	2	Heather St. Johns	0	
Round 3	Epsom & Ewell	1	St. Neots Town	2	
Round 3	Formby	2	Tadcaster Albion	3	
Round 3	Gornal Athletic	0	Runcorn Town	3	
Round 3	Gresley	4	Bustleholme	2	
Round 3	Guildford City	4	Moneyfields	3	
Round 3	Heath Hayes	1	Bloxwich United	3	
Round 3	Herne Bay	2	Colliers Wood United	0	
Round 3	Holbrook Sports	4	St. Helens Town	0	
Round 3	Lancing	4	Witham Town	2	(aet)
Round 3	Leeds Carnegie	1	Staveley Miners Welfare	4	
Round 3	Leiston	3	Hythe Town	1	
Round 3	Leverstock Green	3	Tunbridge Wells	1	
Round 3	Plymouth Parkway	1	Bodmin Town	3	(aet)
Round 3	Poole Town	3	Wantage Town	2	
Round 3	Scarborough Athletic	0	Spennymoor Town	3	
Round 3	Shildon	0	Coalville Town	2	
Round 3	St. Blazey	1	Bemerton Heath Harlequins	2	
Round 3	Stanway Rovers	0	Stansted	1	
Round 3	Stotfold	0	Long Buckby	3	
Round 3	Three Bridges	1	Rye United	3	(aet)
Round 3	Tring Athletic	1	Dunstable Town	6	
Round 3	Verwood Town	2	Torpoint Athletic	5	
Round 3	Westfields	1	Billingham Synthonia	2	(aet)
Round 3	Whitley Bay	7	AFC Liverpool	1	
Round 3	Willand Rovers	2	Bournemouth (Ams)	1	
Round 3	Wroxham	0	St. Ives Town	1	(aet)
Round 4	Billingham Synthonia	2	Tadcaster Albion	1	
Round 4	Bitton	2	Coalville Town	3	
Round 4	Bloxwich United	2	Torpoint Athletic	3	
Round 4	Bodmin Town	1	Stansted	4	
Round 4	Cadbury Heath	1	Spennymoor Town	5	
Round 4	Dunstable Town	2	Willand Rovers	0	
Round 4	Gresley	1	St. Neots Town	3	
Round 4	Guildford City	2	Leiston	6	(aet)
Round 4	Herne Bay	1	Whitley Bay	2	
Round 4	Holbrook Sports	2	Lancing	1	

Round 4	Leverstock Green	4	Bemerton Heath Harlequins	1	
Round 4	Long Buckby	3	Ashington	2	
Round 4	Norton & Stockton Ancients	0	King's Lynn Town	1	
Round 4	Poole Town	3	St. Ives Town	2	
Round 4	Runcorn Town	1	Dunston UTS	3	
Round 4	Staveley Miners Welfare	0	Rye United	3	
Round 5	Coalville Town	3	Holbrook Sports	1	(aet)
Round 5	King's Lynn Town	2	St. Neots Town	1	
Round 5	Leiston	2	Long Buckby	1	
Round 5	Leverstock Green	1	Rye United	2	
Round 5	Poole Town	3	Spennymoor Town	2	
Round 5	Stansted	0	Dunston UTS	2	
Round 5	Torpoint Athletic	1	Billingham Synthonia	0	
Round 5	Whitley Bay	5	Dunstable Town	1	
Round 6	Coalville Town	1	Leiston	0	
Round 6	Dunston UTS	1	Whitley Bay	2	
Round 6	King's Lynn Town	3	Rye United	1	(aet)
Round 6	Poole Town	2	Torpoint Athletic	1	

Semi-finals

1st leg	Coalville Town	3	King's Lynn Town	0	
2nd leg	King's Lynn Town	2	Coalville Town	3	
	Coalville Town won 6-2 on aggregate				
1st leg	Poole Town	1	Whitley Bay	2	
2nd leg	Whitley Bay	3	Poole Town	1	
	Whitley Bay won 5-2 on aggregate				
FINAL	Whitley Bay	3	Coalville Town	2	

Cup Statistics provided by:

www.soccerdata.com

91

Football Conference Blue Square Premier Fixtures 2011/2012 Season

	AFC Telford United	Alfreton Town	Barrow	Bath City	Braintree Town	Cambridge United	Darlington	Ebbsfleet United	Fleetwood Town	Forest Green Rovers	Gateshead	Grimsby Town	Hayes & Yeading United	Kettering Town	Kidderminster Harriers	Lincoln City	Luton Town	Mansfield Town	Newport County	Southport	Stockport County	Tamworth	Wrexham	York City
AFC Telford United		27/09	26/11	17/09	18/02	21/01	31/03	15/10	17/03	04/02	22/10	21/04	01/10	07/01	07/02	23/08	13/08	19/11	27/08	10/03	10/09	09/04	26/12	06/12
Alfreton Town	03/03		20/09	28/04	10/09	24/03	18/02	24/09	18/10	20/08	19/11	07/01	26/11	08/10	21/01	11/10	14/04	07/02	06/12	16/08	04/02	26/12	27/08	09/04
Barrow	08/10	29/11		06/03	24/03	14/04	07/01	03/12	23/08	25/02	27/08	24/01	15/10	18/02	22/10	27/09	04/02	17/09	28/04	09/04	26/12	13/08	10/09	19/11
Bath City	03/12	24/01	20/08		07/01	11/10	08/10	18/02	31/03	09/04	21/04	05/11	04/02	24/09	25/02	17/03	20/09	26/11	26/12	10/09	18/10	27/08	16/08	10/03
Braintree Town	17/12	31/03	28/01	15/10		01/01	22/10	29/08	01/10	19/11	10/03	16/08	06/12	26/02	17/03	03/09	07/04	20/08	17/09	11/02	21/01	27/09	26/11	21/04
Cambridge United	16/08	15/10	11/02	29/11	26/12		24/09	20/09	21/04	10/09	25/02	03/12	27/08	09/04	20/08	22/10	19/11	06/03	24/01	07/01	08/10	28/01	31/03	17/03
Darlington	05/11	23/08	18/10	14/04	13/08	17/12		17/03	21/01	03/12	01/01	07/04	17/09	28/04	15/10	29/08	25/02	03/09	01/10	27/09	03/03	26/11	11/02	28/01
Ebbsfleet United	14/04	11/02	03/09	27/09	09/04	06/12	19/11		17/09	27/08	08/10	18/10	26/12	24/03	29/11	28/04	11/10	28/01	23/08	25/02	06/03	24/01	07/01	13/08
Fleetwood Town	24/09	25/02	06/12	22/10	24/01	18/02	16/08	04/02		08/10	10/09	06/03	20/08	29/11	20/09	14/04	28/04	24/03	11/10	26/12	19/11	07/01	09/04	27/08
Forest Green Rovers	18/10	05/11	31/03	29/08	23/08	03/03	21/04	07/04	28/01		18/02	03/09	17/03	15/10	01/01	17/12	11/02	01/10	27/09	17/09	13/08	06/12	24/01	26/11
Gateshead	28/04	03/09	07/04	11/02	05/11	17/09	26/12	03/03	26/11	14/04		29/08	07/02	20/08	03/12	21/01	17/03	16/08	28/01	18/10	07/01	01/10	11/10	27/09
Grimsby Town	28/01	01/10	11/10	21/01	03/03	23/08	27/08	17/12	13/08	10/03	09/04		10/09	20/09	31/03	01/01	22/10	06/12	19/11	28/04	29/11	17/03	24/09	11/02
Hayes & Yeading	24/03	13/08	17/12	23/08	20/09	07/04	24/01	01/01	01/01	04/12	11/10	24/09		10/03	19/11	11/02	29/08	14/04	29/11	28/01	28/04	04/09	09/10	22/10
Kettering Town	11/02	17/03	21/04	17/12	11/10	29/08	06/12	22/10	03/09	07/02	24/01	26/11	27/09		01/10	28/01	01/01	07/04	13/08	05/11	31/03	17/09	03/03	23/08
Kidderminster Harr.	11/10	17/09	03/03	06/12	18/10	26/11	24/03	10/09	10/03	26/12	13/08	27/09	07/01	14/04		18/02	08/10	28/04	09/04	27/08	23/08	05/11	04/02	24/01
Lincoln City	25/02	15/03	05/11	01/10	14/02	04/02	09/04	26/11	15/10	24/09	20/09	26/12	21/04	10/09	16/08		06/12	18/10	24/03	24/01	27/08	31/03	20/08	07/01
Luton Town	29/11	28/01	01/10	03/03	27/08	27/09	10/09	10/03	05/11	16/08	15/10	24/03	09/04	26/12	21/04	17/09		24/01	07/01	20/08	03/12	18/02	18/10	31/03
Mansfield Town	20/09	22/10	17/03	13/08	03/12	05/11	04/02	31/03	11/02	07/01	29/11	08/10	21/01	27/08	24/09	03/03	23/08		10/09	15/10	09/04	25/02	21/04	26/12
Newport County	07/04	21/04	24/09	01/01	04/02	03/09	10/03	05/11	17/12	21/01	31/03	20/08	16/08	18/10	29/08	03/12	26/11	18/02		08/10	20/09	15/10	17/03	25/02
Southport	03/09	03/12	29/08	19/11	24/09	01/10	14/02	21/04	01/01	29/11	23/08	18/02	31/03	04/02	07/04	13/08	21/01	17/12	03/03		17/03	22/10	20/09	11/10
Stockport County	24/01	17/12	01/01	24/03	14/04	10/03	11/10	20/08	27/09	22/10	06/12	17/09	05/11	16/08	28/01	07/04	03/09	29/08	11/02	26/11		21/04	25/02	01/10
Tamworth	29/08	01/01	21/01	07/04	29/11	28/04	20/08	16/08	03/03	20/09	24/03	04/02	18/10	19/11	11/02	08/10	17/12	10/03	21/02	14/04	24/09		03/12	10/09
Wrexham	01/01	07/04	10/03	28/01	28/04	13/08	29/11	01/10	29/08	24/03	17/12	14/04	18/02	21/01	03/09	19/11	06/03	27/09	22/10	06/12	15/10	23/08		17/09
York City	20/08	29/08	16/08	03/09	08/10	18/10	20/09	21/01	07/04	28/04	04/02	15/10	03/03	03/12	17/12	29/11	24/09	01/01	14/04	24/03	18/02	06/03	05/11	

Please note that the above fixtures may be subject to change.

Football Conference Blue Square North Fixtures 2011/2012 Season	Altrincham	Bishop's Stortford	Blyth Spartans	Boston United	Colwyn Bay	Corby Town	Droylsden	Eastwood Town	FC Halifax Town	Gainsborough Trinity	Gloucester City	Guiseley	Harrogate Town	Hinckley United	Histon	Hyde	Nuneaton Town	Solihull Moors	Stalybridge Celtic	Vauxhall Motors	Worcester City	Workington
Altrincham	■	10/03	18/02	08/10	07/01	06/12	26/12	05/11	14/04	28/04	19/11	29/08	21/01	21/02	20/08	07/04	24/09	24/03	04/02	25/10	10/09	16/08
Bishop's Stortford	25/02	■	03/12	03/09	13/08	25/10	03/03	28/04	24/03	05/11	08/10	07/01	31/01	29/08	26/12	11/02	07/04	23/08	17/09	14/04	19/11	21/01
Blyth Spartans	17/12	20/08	■	17/09	05/11	21/01	10/09	10/03	16/08	07/04	24/03	06/12	29/08	19/11	11/02	14/04	28/04	04/02	21/02	01/11	08/10	01/01
Boston United	17/03	06/12	07/01	■	29/10	12/11	24/09	26/12	29/08	14/04	25/02	28/04	07/04	20/09	16/08	18/02	21/01	10/09	10/03	20/08	11/02	22/10
Colwyn Bay	20/09	04/02	03/03	14/01	■	22/10	03/12	20/08	11/02	12/11	28/04	07/04	14/04	17/03	10/09	16/08	18/02	24/09	25/10	01/01	17/12	29/08
Corby Town	11/02	17/08	24/09	28/01	24/03	■	29/10	29/08	07/01	03/12	07/04	10/09	28/04	14/01	18/02	20/08	19/11	26/12	08/10	05/11	10/03	14/04
Droylsden	01/01	18/02	28/01	24/03	03/09	17/12	■	14/01	22/10	29/08	14/04	16/08	11/02	17/09	10/03	20/09	20/08	29/11	05/11	28/04	08/11	07/04
Eastwood Town	21/04	20/09	03/09	01/01	14/02	09/04	13/08	■	18/02	25/10	23/08	12/11	17/03	03/03	22/10	24/09	03/12	21/01	31/03	04/02	27/08	17/12
FC Halifax Town	03/12	28/01	12/11	09/04	23/08	13/08	21/04	08/10	■	01/01	17/03	14/02	03/03	17/12	31/03	25/10	04/02	29/10	27/08	17/09	14/01	03/09
Gainsborough Trinity	28/01	10/09	27/08	19/11	31/03	23/08	09/04	24/03	26/12	■	29/10	24/09	18/02	22/10	21/01	07/01	10/03	13/08	06/12	25/02	21/04	20/09
Gloucester City	03/09	17/12	22/10	31/03	17/09	20/09	17/01	28/01	05/11	11/02	■	10/03	12/11	03/12	09/04	29/08	16/08	07/01	21/04	18/02	01/01	20/08
Guiseley	09/04	21/04	23/08	17/12	27/08	31/03	21/01	25/02	20/09	03/03	04/02	■	01/01	13/08	17/03	22/10	29/10	11/02	19/11	03/09	17/09	03/12
Harrogate Town	13/08	29/10	09/04	27/08	06/12	04/02	23/08	19/11	24/09	08/10	10/09	26/12	■	28/01	07/01	14/01	05/11	21/04	25/02	10/03	31/03	24/03
Hinckley United	29/10	09/04	21/04	04/02	08/10	25/02	31/03	07/01	10/09	15/08	27/08	18/02	20/08	■	24/09	12/11	26/12	31/10	21/01	24/03	05/12	10/03
Histon	03/03	01/01	13/08	25/10	25/02	27/08	04/02	14/04	19/11	17/12	14/01	28/01	17/09	07/04	■	28/04	24/03	06/12	03/09	08/10	23/08	29/10
Hyde	27/08	31/03	29/10	21/04	19/11	13/02	25/02	05/12	10/03	17/09	21/01	24/03	03/09	22/08	05/11	■	08/10	09/04	01/01	17/12	13/08	04/02
Nuneaton Town	31/03	27/08	14/01	23/08	21/04	03/03	25/10	17/09	25/02	03/09	06/12	07/02	17/12	01/01	20/09	17/03	■	22/10	13/08	28/01	09/04	12/11
Solihull Moors	17/09	12/11	17/03	05/11	10/03	01/01	08/10	16/08	28/04	14/01	25/10	20/08	03/12	03/09	29/08	28/01	14/04	■	17/12	07/04	18/02	25/02
Stalybridge Celtic	22/10	14/01	20/09	03/12	28/01	17/03	07/01	10/09	07/04	20/08	24/09	14/04	16/08	28/04	12/11	26/12	11/02	03/03	■	29/08	29/10	18/02
Vauxhall Motors	23/08	22/10	31/03	21/02	26/12	21/04	12/11	29/10	21/01	17/03	13/08	14/01	20/09	11/02	03/12	03/03	10/09	27/08	09/04	■	07/01	24/09
Worcester City	12/11	24/09	25/02	03/03	21/01	03/09	17/03	07/04	20/08	04/02	26/12	04/11	22/10	14/04	30/01	03/12	29/08	19/09	24/03	15/08	■	28/04
Workington	14/01	17/03	26/12	13/08	09/04	17/09	27/08	11/02	06/12	21/02	03/03	08/10	25/10	05/11	21/04	10/09	07/01	31/03	23/08	19/11	28/01	■

Please note that the above fixtures may be subject to change.

Football Conference Blue Square South Fixtures 2011/2012 Season	Basingstoke Town	Boreham Wood	Bromley	Chelmsford City	Dartford	Dorchester Town	Dover Athletic	Eastbourne Borough	Eastleigh	Farnborough	Hampton & Richmond Borough	Havant & Waterlooville	Maidenhead United	Salisbury City	Staines Town	Sutton United	Thurrock	Tonbridge Angels	Truro City	Welling United	Weston-super-Mare	Woking
Basingstoke Town		29/10	17/03	17/12	03/09	17/09	10/03	21/04	21/01	24/09	29/08	31/03	01/01	03/12	25/10	20/08	25/02	06/03	04/02	12/11	16/08	07/04
Boreham Wood	22/08		05/11	03/12	08/10	10/03	12/11	18/02	24/03	14/04	11/02	13/08	24/10	07/01	09/04	26/12	27/08	28/04	10/09	19/09	21/01	28/01
Bromley	07/01	16/08		25/02	09/04	12/11	25/10	03/12	10/03	24/03	29/10	04/02	20/08	10/09	11/02	27/08	21/04	26/12	21/01	24/09	31/03	20/09
Chelmsford City	24/03	24/09	19/11		27/08	29/10	03/09	09/04	24/10	22/08	03/03	18/02	05/12	14/04	21/01	07/01	26/12	19/09	13/08	10/03	04/02	28/04
Dartford	14/01	21/04	29/08	07/04		17/12	03/12	16/08	10/09	10/03	20/08	14/03	31/03	25/02	20/09	11/02	28/01	24/09	22/10	01/01	12/11	29/10
Dorchester Town	05/11	22/10	28/04	11/02	24/03		21/01	20/08	27/08	06/12	13/03	25/02	16/08	26/12	14/04	19/11	07/01	28/01	09/04	10/09	20/09	24/09
Dover Athletic	10/09	31/03	06/12	06/03	23/08	13/08		26/12	07/01	20/09	14/01	24/09	21/04	28/01	24/03	09/04	22/10	27/08	18/02	25/02	05/11	19/11
Eastbourne Borough	19/11	17/09	23/08	29/08	14/02	14/01	01/01		08/10	13/08	14/04	03/09	28/01	28/04	25/02	10/03	11/02	25/10	29/10	07/04	17/12	24/03
Eastleigh	13/08	17/12	03/09	21/04	19/11	07/04	17/03	31/03		03/03	17/09	01/01	05/11	14/01	24/09	28/01	06/12	11/02	25/02	22/10	29/08	23/08
Farnborough	28/01	14/01	17/12	05/11	17/09	31/03	11/02	06/03	12/11		07/04	21/04	29/08	17/08	10/09	22/10	08/10	25/02	03/12	20/08	17/03	01/01
Hampton & Richmond	09/04	06/12	13/08	10/09	21/01	23/08	04/02	05/11	18/02	27/08		22/10	17/03	06/03	26/12	31/03	19/11	07/01	10/03	21/04	24/09	25/02
Havant & Waterlooville	11/02	03/03	08/10	20/08	07/01	25/10	14/04	12/11	26/12	29/10	28/01		14/01	09/04	28/04	10/09	17/09	24/03	27/08	16/08	03/12	10/03
Maidenhead United	26/12	25/02	22/10	08/10	04/02	03/12	29/10	07/01	28/04	09/04	12/11	13/09		24/03	27/08	21/01	23/08	13/08	20/09	11/02	10/09	14/04
Salisbury City	20/09	17/03	18/02	22/10	05/11	01/01	03/03	24/09	04/02	19/11	03/09	29/08	17/12		10/03	21/04	13/08	06/12	23/08	31/03	07/04	21/01
Staines Town	03/03	29/08	17/09	16/08	06/12	08/10	17/12	17/03	14/02	18/02	01/01	19/11	07/04	20/08		05/11	03/09	14/01	31/03	04/02	21/04	22/10
Sutton United	18/02	01/01	07/04	17/03	14/04	03/09	29/08	04/02	20/09	28/04	03/12	06/03	24/09	25/10	23/08		14/01	29/10	12/11	17/12	25/02	13/08
Thurrock	14/04	07/04	14/02	01/01	25/10	17/03	16/08	20/09	29/10	04/02	28/04	21/01	18/02	12/11	03/12	03/03		10/09	24/09	29/08	20/08	17/12
Tonbridge Angels	22/10	04/02	01/01	31/03	03/03	21/04	07/04	21/01	20/08	03/09	08/10	17/12	10/03	17/09	12/11	16/08	05/11		17/03	03/12	18/02	29/08
Truro City	08/10	13/03	14/04	14/01	28/04	29/08	20/08	03/03	16/08	25/10	17/12	07/04	03/09	11/02	28/01	17/09	24/03	19/11		05/11	01/01	06/12
Welling United	28/04	19/11	03/03	28/01	26/12	18/02	08/10	27/08	14/04	21/01	25/10	06/12	17/09	29/10	13/08	24/03	09/04	23/08	07/01		06/03	03/09
Weston-super-Mare	06/12	03/09	28/01	17/09	13/08	03/03	28/04	22/10	09/04	07/01	24/03	23/08	19/11	27/08	29/10	08/10	10/03	14/04	26/12	14/01		11/02
Woking	27/08	20/08	14/01	12/11	18/02	04/02	17/09	10/09	03/12	26/12	16/08	05/11	03/03	08/10	07/01	13/12	31/03	09/04	21/04	17/03	25/10	

Please note that the above fixtures may be subject to change.